MEASURING THE EARTH WITH A STICK

Science as I've Seen It

Bob McDonald

VIKING

Viking

Published by the Penguin Group

Penguin Books Canada Ltd, 10 Alcorn Avenue, Toronto, Ontario, Canada M4V 3B2

Penguin Books Ltd, 27 Wrights Lane, London W8 5TZ, England

Penguin Putnam Inc., 375 Hudson Street, New York, New York 10014, U.S.A.

Penguin Books Australia Ltd, Ringwood, Victoria, Australia

Penguin Books (NZ) Ltd, crn Rosedale and Airborne roads, Albany, Auckland 1310, New Zealand

Penguin Books Ltd, Registered Offices: Harmondsworth, Middlesex, England

First published 2000

10 9 8 7 6 5 4 3 2 1

Copyright © Bob McDonald 2000

Illustrations © Dave Sheridan 2000

Printed and bound in Canada on acid free paper.

Text design and typesetting by Laura Brady

Canadian Cataloguing in Publication Data

McDonald, Bob, 1951–

    Measuring the earth with a stick: science as I've seen it

ISBN 0-670-88925-3

1. Science – Popular works. I. Title.

Q171.M28 2000   500   C00-931632-9

Visit Penguin Canada's web site at **www.penguin.ca**

To Sandy
For inspiration and support

CONTENTS

Acknowledgements

I WISH TO THANK Eva Turley, at the Hospital for Sick Children, Dr. Gary Rollman of the University of Western Ontario, Barbara Berson, Cheryl Cohen, dozens of producers and technicians who put me on the air and more than three thousand scientists who have responded to my questions over the last twenty-five years.

PREFACE

THIS IS A DIARY OF a traveller, one who has been fortunate to explore many parts of this planet out of pure curiosity and one who has journeyed along the edge of human knowledge as a journalist. It's an extreme pleasure to watch science happen. I've been introduced to some of the brightest minds alive today, people who have changed the way I see the world. And it is that perspective I would like to share with you.

When a new science story makes headlines, the first reaction is usually, "Gee, I didn't know that!" Then we get on with our daily lives. But look deeper into that story and something else emerges, a different perspective on ourselves, something I call the poetry of science. Just as poets provide different perspectives on our lives, our relationships or just an appreciation of the beauty that surrounds us, scientists see the universe in ways that provide a perspective like no other. Whether it is our minuscule part in an unimaginably large cosmos or the universe within a drop of water, a beauty emerges that was unseen before, the poetry of science, or perhaps I should say the poetry of nature seen through the eyes of science.

1

It's that poetic side that I look for when following science stories, and it often shows up in surprising places, like a parking lot. While reporting on a pollution story, I was looking at oil drippings from a car when the sun emerged from a cloud and shone on the filmy surface at just the right angle, creating a beautiful spectrum of colours that would rival any rainbow. Even when we assault her, nature manages to shine through.

Scientists are not afraid to admit this poetic side of their work, although they are seldom asked about it. The hallways of astronomy departments are lined with colourful photographs of distant galaxies just because they are so beautiful to look at. In fact, most astronomy is not done with pictures: information usually comes in the form of boring numbers about luminosity, brightness and spectra. Photographs don't actually provide much information at all, yet astronomers keep taking pictures because galaxies and interstellar clouds are natural works of art. A mathematician looking at those same photographs might marvel at how the curve that defines the spiral shape of a galaxy is the same as that found in seashells.

When you think about it, the world according to our five senses is not a very exciting place. The Earth looks flat and everything happens within a few kilometres of where we are standing. But thanks to the people who look through microscopes and telescopes, we see millions of life forms swarming around us, on us, in us, and we see stars beneath our feet. The scientists who have that perspective and an ability to articulate it have given me an appreciation of the world that has had a big impact on my personal travels, sort of a *Lonely Planet* guide to a planet.

In 1979 I took half a year off and travelled all the way

around the world by myself just to see what the Earth looks like. It was the best education I ever had. But thanks to a little bit of scientific knowledge, I saw more than stunning scenery and other ways of life: I saw mountains pushed skyward by the force of continents in collision, volcanoes punching holes in the crust of the planet and so many stars that I almost fell off the side of the Earth one night in Africa.

Another advantage to being a journalist is that you get to play with all the scientific toys. I've been strapped into contraptions of all sorts designed to test the human body for space flight, driven prototype vehicles, even jumped out of an airplane without a parachute. It's provided a deeper appreciation for the brave souls who buckle themselves inside these machines and soar over our heads, making it look easy along the way.

Then there are the smart machines that boldly go where no humans can go, the robots that have ventured out to other planets.

Finally, there are the visual artists, poets of a different kind who bring to life what science has already revealed but could not bring into our direct vision: alien landscapes, ancient human ancestors, the inside of an atom. In fact, it was an unknown artist's perspective on Saturn that first got me interested in other worlds when I was six years old; later, space artist Jon Lomberg introduced me to the galaxy; and today Dave Sheridan is helping convey some of my ideas to you through his illustrations in this book.

You won't find all areas of science represented here, and it's not all gee-whiz stuff either. I've even learned a few lessons about pain and death. These are events that have enriched my life, that might provide a little insight into how I see the world.

So come take a journey with me around the world, through time, into space, even from the deck of my boat and meet some of the fascinating characters who have changed my perspective through this amazing looking-glass we call science.

Part One
Skyscapes

THE NIGHT I ALMOST FELL OFF THE EARTH

*An African sky illuminates
our place in the cosmos*

STARS SHIMMER BENEATH MY feet. A wall of Earth against my back rises straight above my head. I cling to the vertical face like a fly, convinced that losing my grip would leave me tumbling forever in the empty void before me. Yes, it was a close call the night I almost slipped off the side of the planet, the night I experienced the most intense case of cosmic vertigo in my life and got my first true sense of planet Earth's place in the cosmos.

The hillside that carried me on this cosmic journey is in East Africa where I had joined a group of fellow astronomy buffs on a 1979 expedition to see a total eclipse of the Sun in Tanzania. An eclipse is one of those rare events where nature performs a relatively simple act, the Moon casts a shadow on the Earth; but the awesome spectacle of the Moon passing in front of the Sun, turning day into night, is worth travelling great distances to see. Because of the complex motions of the Earth and the Moon, the narrow shadow of the Moon passes over a different part of the Earth's surface every time. The shadow itself is only a few kilometres wide so you must be directly in it to see the full effect. Eclipse paths are well known ahead of time, which makes them great vacation planners to exotic parts of the world. This trip included a safari across the Serengeti plains, a climb up Mount Kilimanjaro as well as my first opportunity to see the magnificent stars of the African skies.

The bottom half of the Earth, the part south of the equator, points towards the centre of our Milky Way galaxy, a region packed with many more stars than the section of the sky we see in the North. That's a strange irony because most of the world's largest telescopes are in the Northern Hemisphere. Having spent many nights in Canadian wilderness marvelling at our view of the Milky Way, I was looking forward to an even better show in Africa. The opportunity came at a magnificent lodge perched on the rim of the East African Rift Valley, one of the largest single valleys on Earth. It's actually a place where two sections of the Earth's crust are pulling apart, ripping a huge 4,500 kilometre gouge down the length of the African continent. The view from the rim, three kilometres above the valley floor, affords one of the best panoramas of the African savanna during the day and an unobstructed view of the clear southern skies at night.

Long after dusk had faded from the western horizon, my fellow space enthusiasts and I stood outside trying to outdo each other naming constellations that are not visible in Canada. But as interesting as it was to spot the star Alpha Centauri, our closest neighbour, there isn't much more to say about a star once you've spotted it. The closest star to us is not the brightest: other hotter stars give off more light. In fact, Alpha Centauri looks like any other star in the sky, and if you didn't know where it was you would miss it completely. I really wanted to see the Milky Way, but to do that I had to get away from the lights of the lodge.

I walked about a kilometre along the rim of the valley then climbed down a short distance and lay on the slope in the stubby grass. The ever-present symphony of African insects provided a soothing background as warm night breezes drifted up from the valley below.

It's amazing how much time we spend looking downwards, especially at night as we tread carefully over unfamiliar ground. When we just take the time to stop and look upwards, the immensity of the night sky actually sinks in, especially in Africa where dry air provides a transparent window on the universe. When you're alone on the hill with no lights from human activity in sight and no trees to block the stars, the view of the sky is so panoramic you can't take it all in at once. The stars seem to completely surround you.

My fully dilated pupils drink in every photon of light that rains down from the heavens. The longer I look, the more stars come into view, shimmering diamonds turning themselves on one after another sprinkle across the blackness, filling the dark spaces. I see the sky as it appeared to our human ancestors who walked this same region millions of years ago. Even the void between the stars seems blacker. With more stars before me than I have ever seen in one place, I feel like an astronaut floating in space.

From the high perspective of the hillside, stars extend all the way down to the horizon well below my line of sight. Then there is the Milky Way, the sight I came so far to see, rising straight up out of the horizon forming a complete luminous arch that reaches overhead across the entire sky. Lying there on a rather steep slope makes the sky appear in front of me rather than above. I have to dig my heels into the soil to keep my body from slowly creeping down the slope, creating the illusion of being a fly clinging to a wall. In fact, this perspective isn't an illusion at all. Tanzania really is on the side of the Earth, so I am clinging to an earthen wall. The planet is behind me, and as my body begins to slide down the slope, I dig in my heels, feeling that if I let go I will drop off the side of the world and fall forever into a very big black space.

With up and down in their proper positions, I begin to get a true sense of planet Earth as a ball floating in space, surrounded on all sides by an incredibly starry sky.

We know the Earth is a sphere, we know it moves through space, and lying there that night looking out into that incredibly deep sky, I could almost feel its roundness curving away in all directions from the centre of my back. The immense size of the great ball I was clinging to began to impress itself on my consciousness, although I couldn't quite grasp the full scale. That's not surprising when you consider the simple fact that to all our human senses, the Earth doesn't look like a ball at all; it looks quite flat. Sure, there are hills and hollows, but subtract all the valleys from all the mountains and you end up with a plane, flat as a pancake. Take a walk in any direction and you will eventually come to an ocean. No wonder some ancient cultures depicted the Earth as an island floating in a circular sea under the dome of the sky; after all that's what it looks like to our five senses. It's quite a remarkable leap of faith to abandon what appears to be common sense and believe our scientific measurements of the Earth as a sphere floating in nothingness. As I clung to the side of the planet in Tanzania, that scientific knowledge turned the night sky into a three-dimensional space through which I was hurtling at terrific speeds.

Actually, the idea of a round Earth is not new. Around 350 BC, Aristotle came up with what he believed was conclusive proof that the Earth was a sphere. He pointed out that when you travel north, new stars appear over the horizon ahead of you that were not visible from where you started, while those normally visible back home disappear below the horizon behind you. He also pointed to ships disappearing hull first over the horizon and finally to the curved shape of the Earth's shadow on the Moon during a lunar eclipse. But these arguments were academic without some experiment that could actually measure the planet. That opportunity came about a hundred years later, thanks to a simply elegant experiment carried out by a very ingenious Greek mathematician and astronomer named Eratosthenes. He made the first accurate measurement of the circumference of Earth around 200 BC, and he did it with a stick.

This astounding bit of calculation is so simple that any school kid could do it today; in fact, one Canadian Internet project has already done it. Eratosthenes worked in the great library of Alexandria, considered to be the largest gathering of knowledge in the ancient world. The library was located at the mouth of the Nile, along the south shore of the Mediterranean. Although he worked in the library, Eratosthenes' hometown was Syene, an Egyptian city 900 kilometres south of Alexandria, and it was there, while on vacation, that he began his measurement of the Earth. He probably didn't actually set out to measure the planet because he was, after all, on vacation, but a good scientist is always on the lookout for interesting phenomena, and one sunny day in June, he stumbled upon just such an event while crossing a town square. There happened to be a well in the square and like any curious tourist with time on his hands, he looked down it to see how deep it was. To his surprise, he saw the Sun reflected in the water at the bottom. What a coincidence: he had chosen the exact moment when the Sun was passing directly overhead. Now, being an astronomer, Eratosthenes knew that there are very few times when the Sun is straight overhead. Its position changes with the seasons. This particular day was June 21st, the summer solstice in the Northern Hemisphere, when the Sun is at its most northerly and highest position in the sky. In Syene, that is the only day when the Sun would be reflected in the bottom of the well. On any other day, the Sun would be farther south so it would be at an angle to the well, assuming of course that the well diggers went straight down.

Like many Greek scholars at the time, Eratosthenes believed that the Earth was round. After all, the Moon and Sun are round, why should the Earth be any different? He reasoned that if it was flat, then on June 21st, the Sun would reflect in the bottom of every well on Earth because rays of light from the Sun come straight down from the sky in parallel lines. If the Earth was round, the Sun could be seen in only one well at a time because the curvature of the Earth's surface would place all the other wells at different angles to the Sun. Water wells point straight down towards the centre of the Earth like the spokes of a wheel pointing to the hub. All he needed to do was find a well in another location on the same day to prove whether the Earth was flat or round.

Unfortunately, June 21st only comes once a year so he had to wait a while to complete his experiment. On the following summer solstice, Eratosthenes was back at his job in the library of Alexandria but he didn't forget his noontime rendezvous with the Sun. There was no water well nearby so he used a gnomon, an instrument astronomers use to measure the position of the Sun in the sky. It's a relative of the sundial and works in a similar way. A gnomon is basically two sticks that form an L-shape. One stick is laid flat on the ground so the other one points straight up. The stick lying flat has a scale on it which measures the angle of the shadow cast by the upright stick. That angle is the elevation of the Sun in the sky. If the Sun passes straight overhead, there is no shadow at all. The gnomon is a handy tool to track the passage of the seasons by measuring how high the Sun rises above the horizon. On this day, however, Eratosthenes used it to measure the Earth. He knew that if the Sun's shadow disappeared at noon the Earth would be flat.

He was probably delighted and somewhat relieved when precisely at noon a small sliver of a shadow remained on the gnomon, measuring only seven degrees. That meant the surface of the Earth was curved between the two cities of Alexandria and Syene, a curve which formed an angle of seven degrees. Think of the spokes of a wheel. Only one spoke can point straight up at a time. A spoke next to it will be at a slight angle because it is farther along the curve of the rim. The point where the spokes meet at the hub of the wheel is where the angle is formed. The farther apart the spokes are, the greater that angle.

Eratosthenes made a simple calculation and figured out that seven degrees is about one-fiftieth of a circle. That means the distance between the two cities was one-fiftieth of the distance around the entire Earth. He knew that Syene was about five thousand stadiums south of Alexandria, so he multiplied that distance by fifty to get the circumference of the Earth. There is some debate about the exact length of the ancient Greek stadium, but converting an average estimate of its length into kilometres, the calculation for the circumference of the Earth made by Eratosthenes works out to about 42,000 kilometres, almost bang on.

If I could travel back in time, that is a moment I would choose to visit, the moment Eratosthenes made his astounding calculation. There were probably lots of people walking past paying no attention to him but I would casually ask, "Hey, mister, what are you doing with that stick?"

"Oh, I just measured the size of the Earth with it."

"Sure, fellah."

Standing there scribbling a few numbers, then making a simple calculation in his head must have been an over-whelming moment for Eratosthenes as he realized the true size of the Earth. The known world at that time was basically the land around the Mediterranean Sea and a bit of Africa. To realize that the world is vastly larger than anyone imagined must have been unbelievable. What thoughts went through his head that day? Fortunately for us, he thought the result of his experiment was important enough to record it for future scholars to ponder.

Lying on the hillside in Tanzania, feeling the great sphere of the Earth behind my back I felt somehow connected to Eratosthenes, trying to grasp the sheer size of the planet. I'm not sure I succeeded. But I do have a slight advantage over the ancient Greek. Modern astronomy tells us more than just the shape and size of the Earth; we now know it moves through space in several different ways. I wasn't just a fly on the wall—the wall was moving.

The idea of a moving Earth was not quick to catch on among learned society. Good old terra firma seems pretty firm and steady beneath our feet, yet every day we all travel completely around the world, or rather the world carries us around itself as it rotates. That's a long way to go in only twenty-four hours and, depending on where you live, you can be travelling very fast to make it on time. Near the equator in Africa I was moving at about 1,600 km/h towards the east while clinging to that hillside. Farther away from the equator the speed decreases, so people in southern Ontario are doing about 1,000 km/h while someone standing at the North or South Pole is rotating on the spot at half the speed of the hour hand of a clock.

That old saying "Stop the world I want to get off" takes on new meaning when you consider that if it did suddenly stop most of us would be plastered against the east wall at about the speed of a fighter jet.

Once again, our senses don't pick up this motion; the Earth is such a smooth spaceship we don't feel it move, although we can watch the passage of the stars as we spin around every night, or simply watch a sunset. It looks like the ruby red Sun sinks below the horizon, but it's really the Earth rolling us around to the night side. For many ancient scholars, these movements of the heavenly bodies were not enough proof that the Earth turns. It seemed more reasonable to trust what our senses tell us and believe that the sky rotates while we stand still beneath it. In the fifteenth century Galileo was charged with heresy by the Inquisition for believing in a moving Earth, a charge that was not recanted by the church until 1989. What was needed was another conclusive experiment, a clear demonstration that the Earth really turns. That demonstration didn't arrive until 1851.

French physicist Jean Bernard Léon Foucault performed another elegant experiment using the simplest equipment, a weight on the end of a string. He predicted that a pendulum swinging for twenty-four hours would appear to change its orientation in a counterclockwise direction and make one complete circle in that time. In reality the pendulum would remain fixed in space while the Earth turns under it. Using the dome of a church in Paris Foucault swung a giant pendulum for 24 hours and sure enough its orientation shifted at exactly the proper rate. Foucault pendulums are often found swinging in the lobbies of science museums today, although most visitors pass them by not appreciating their ability to demonstrate one of the most fundamental principles of science . . . the Earth turns.

During my evening on the rim of the East African Rift Valley the Earth had turned me around to its the dark side, but I knew it was also carrying me in another direction at the same time. I was whizzing around the Sun at the unbelievable speed of 108,000 km/h, almost three times the speed of the space shuttle. Our speedy planet will move a hundred kilometres in the time it takes you to read this sentence. But again, we don't feel it or see that motion easily. Space is so empty that there are no trees or signposts whizzing by to show how fast we're moving, although every now and then bits of road dirt do bounce off our planet's windshield.

One of the few opportunities to actually see the speed of the Earth as it travels through space occurs every August during the Perseid Meteor shower, when brilliant streaks of light flash across the night sky in nature's silent fireworks display. The streaks are tiny grains of cosmic dust that burn up when they run into our atmosphere. But it's not just the dust running into the Earth that's causing the light show; it's also the speed of the Earth running into the dust. Every summer our planet ploughs through a trail of dust left behind by a comet, much like the dust cloud left behind a truck speeding down a dirt road. In the same way bits of dirt and pebbles bounce off the windshield of your car when you pass a truck, the bits of space dirt hit our atmospheric windshield. The tiny pieces of grit, about the size of a grain of sand, are moving so quickly they are vaporized instantly by friction with the air. Meteors in a shower always start from one spot in the sky, such as the constellation Perseus, and radiate outwards from that point. That's purely an effect of the Earth's motion through space, just as snowflakes, reflecting in headlights, seem to be coming straight at your car when in fact it's the motion of the car moving through the snow that creates the illusion. Meteor showers are an opportunity to look down the road in space that the Earth follows on its journey around the Sun and see how fast it moves.

There were no meteors in the skies over Tanzania to give me a sense of motion. In fact, when I thought about the time of night and position of the stars at that hour, it turned out that I was on the back side of the planet as it moved through space, so I was looking backwards down the road. That perspective enhanced the fly-on-the-wall feeling as the Earth seemed to be racing away from behind my back. If I lost my grip I would be left dangling out there in space. I hung on to the grass a little tighter.

The fear of falling off the Earth was enhanced further by a powerful feeling of depth as I looked out among the stars of the Milky Way. The luminous arch of light that reaches across the entire sky is the largest single structure visible to the naked eye, yet most people seldom see it. The subtle glow of our home galaxy is easily washed out by city lights or even the light of a full Moon. It takes truly black skies to really appreciate the Milky Way. Before the spread of cities, the blue band of light figured prominently in ancient mythology as a pathway to the netherworld, a stairway to heaven, even the handle of a great basket that holds the Earth like an egg in a nest. But all these images of the Milky Way are basically two-dimensional lines across the sky, which according to our inaccurate senses is how it looks. And basically, that two-dimensional perspective of our galaxy didn't change until very modern times.

How far away is the Milky Way? Since we can't go out there with a measuring stick, charting the distance to the stars has led to gross mistakes, similar to the errors in judging the size of the Earth. The problem is, stars look pretty much alike, just points of light in the blackness. But if you watch them carefully enough through highly sensitive instruments, you will see that they move—and I'm not talking just about the nightly procession across the sky, which is due to the turning of the Earth. Stars move in very subtle ways relative to each other, like people shuffling in a crowd. It was that motion that provided one of the first modern measuring sticks for the universe.

For centuries sky watchers have made pictures out of star patterns: animals, gods, dippers and teapots. The constellations we see today are basically the same shapes our ancestors saw millions of years ago. But since the development of extremely precise instruments, astronomers have been able to see that these still pictures are in fact movies. The stars are slowly moving with respect to one another at different speeds, in different directions, all following a grand order dictated by the laws of the universe on an unimaginably colossal scale that reaches all the way back to the beginning of time.

The first motion to be noticed among the stars is a slight wobble back and forth, a wobble that takes exactly a year to happen. Only some stars do this and the fact that their wobble is exactly the same period as the Earth's year was the clue that in fact it's not the stars moving at all, it's us. As the Earth swings around the Sun our perspective on the stars changes from season to season the way objects in a room appear to move with respect to each other when you move your head back and forth. It's called parallax.

Using the 300-million-kilometre diameter of the Earth's

orbit around the Sun as a way of moving our collective heads from side to side, astronomers have been able to see stars close to us moving back and forth while more distant stars remain fixed, an effective tool to measure distance. But parallax only works for stars that are relatively close. As telescopes became more powerful they could see stars so far away they don't wobble at all. A bigger measuring stick was needed.

Fortunately there are other tricks for measuring distances within the universe although they become less accurate the farther out we go. The next time you see a truly black starry sky, a bit of a rarity these days as cities grow larger, look carefully and you will see that stars are not all the same—some are brighter than others and some come in different colours, like ornamental light bulbs. That's not an illusion. Stars do come in different colours because they burn at different temperatures. Hot stars are blue, cool stars are red. Our Sun is an average yellow. If the stars were indeed light bulbs, and we knew their wattage, it would be easy to measure their distance: We would just measure how bright they are.

Stand under a street lamp at night and look down along the row of lamps lining the street. You will see how the lamps in the distance do not look as bright as the one over your head and the farther away they are, the dimmer they look. So you can use that difference in brightness to measure the distance of the lamps down the street.

Astronomers do the same thing with stars. The Sun is like the overhead street lamp. We know how bright it is and how far away it is, so the distance to other stars can be figured out by measuring how much dimmer they appear than the Sun. Of course this technique assumes that all stars are exactly like the Sun, which they are not. In the same way you could not use the street lamp as a reference to measure the distance of a flashlight, unless you had a flashlight with you. In other words, if you had a pocket full of every type of light bulb, you could measure the distance of all bulbs within sight.

Astronomers have spent a great deal of time figuring out how bright different types of stars would be if they were as close as the Sun and come up with a fairly good picture of how far away the stars are . . . and they're really far. So far, in fact, that Earthly measuring sticks of kilometres and miles lose their meaning. Even the closest star to Earth, Alpha Centauri, is about 42 million, million kilometres away, give or take a few million. Go to any other star and the numbers get so large they're ridiculous to deal with let alone understand. So astronomers prefer to use the time it would take a beam of light to cover that distance, the light year. By that measure, Alpha Centauri is only four and a half light years away. All the stars you can see with the naked eye are within a few hundred light years of Earth. Telescopes see stars millions of light years away.

From the Southern Hemisphere, where I lay that night, the sky is littered with multicoloured stars hanging in the blackness like tiny Christmas ornaments, a truly three-dimensional space. But there is more to the night sky than stars. Rising behind them all is the glow of the Milky Way, a collection of so many stars they fuse together into a diffuse halo that circles the entire sky.

It wasn't until the 1920s that American astronomer Edwin Hubble proved that the Milky Way is an organization of stars forming an enormous disc about 100,000 light years across. The arch of light across the night sky that we see as the Milky Way is that disc seen from the inside. We don't have a picture of what it looks like on the outside because it's so big we would have to travel for thousands of years at the speed of light just to get far enough away to see it all, in the same way astronauts had to travel a third of the way to the Moon to see the whole Earth.

Then, peering deeper into space, Hubble discovered that our galaxy is only one of many others, galaxies made up of billions of stars organized into beautiful shapes: whirlpools, footballs, some just irregular blobs.

Most importantly, Hubble found that they are all racing away from us at tremendous speed, the genesis of the expanding universe idea. It was an Eratosthenes-type revelation where the universe suddenly became a lot larger. And if all the galaxies are rushing away from each other today, they must have been closer together in the past. Run the movie backwards all the way to the beginning and they must have been clumped together into one unimaginably small and dense object that somehow blew up . . . the big bang theory of creation. But even though this was a profound revelation it left a basic question unanswered, one that Hubble never saw resolved: how big and therefore how old is the universe? Another measuring stick was needed.

Galaxies are millions of light years away, which makes it difficult to see individual stars; however, there are the occasional flare-ups, where stars explode as spectacular supernovae that for a brief time outshine their entire galaxy. These can be seen across intergalactic space, making them light bulbs for measuring the distances to galaxies. When the space telescope that bears Hubble's name was launched into orbit, and after its faulty mirror was corrected, it searched the heavens for exploding stars. Along with new high-technology telescopes on the ground a puzzling answer came in . . . the universe seemed to be a lot younger than anyone thought . . . too young for some astronomers.

Dr. Peter Stetson, from the Dominion Astrophysical Observatory in Penticton, B.C., told me in an interview, "Well Bob, we've got a problem. The universe seems to be younger than some of the stars that are in it, which is clearly impossible. That's like a mother being younger than her own children."

The new, refined measurements of distant galaxies lowered the age of the universe to ten billion years, possibly even as low as eight. Some stars live for twelve billion years. Clearly there was a mistake, which has since been more or less resolved, although the astronomers are still vague when they say the universe is twelve to fifteen billion years old, give or take a few billion.

Throughout all of this galaxy-hunting the big revelation that came from Hubble's work was the fact that we are living in one of these galaxies. That Milky Way crossing the night sky is an unimaginably huge disc of several hundred billion stars, all swirling around a glowing centre and strung out in curving spiral arms. Hubble called it an "Island Universe," which is a good name considering how vast and complex it is.

The strange irony is that our telescopes capture beautiful images of galaxies all over the universe, but we don't have a picture of our home galaxy because we live inside it. Our position within the Milky Way is like a person standing on a downtown street trying to see the shape of the whole city. It would be nice if we could fly above our city of stars and look down on it like passengers in an airliner, but it will be quite a while before we get that view. Our galaxy is simply too large to see all at once. Even if we had the benefit of warp drive, a spaceship like the *Starship Enterprise* would need thousands of years to get above the galaxy to see it all in one view. One thing is clear, when we do get that outside picture of the Milky Way it will be absolutely stunning.

In the meantime, we can look at other sister galaxies for a clue to our own appearance and using radio telescopes to peer through cosmic dust, astronomers have come up with a reasonable map of what the Milky Way actually looks like . . . a giant Frisbee. We know the Sun is only one of a vast multitude of stars arranged in a giant flat disc that slowly rotates in space. If all the stars were grains of sand, they would cover your living-room carpet up to your knees. The whole disc of the galaxy takes about 200 million years just to turn once. The last time it was in its present position, dinosaurs were just beginning to stomp through the grass on Earth. As it slowly turns, the stars swirl into an immense whirlpool, sweeping the Sun along the inside edge of one of the spiral arms about two-thirds out from the centre. Everything about the Milky Way is so far beyond human scale it's difficult to grasp the magnitude. And while many scientists have attempted to describe the astounding aspects of our home galaxy, the one person who gave me the best sense of the Milky Way was a man who tried to build it.

My first encounter with Jon Lomberg was in a windowless room deep in the bowels of the Ontario Science Centre. He had been brought in to produce a painting of the Milky Way for the Hall of Space. I was an instructor in the astronomy department at the time and wanted to see what he was doing. When the door to the small room opened, a young man about my own age slightly covered in paint speckles peered out from the darkness. There were no lights on in the room.

Stepping into the room I could see strips of cardboard taped around the edges of the door to ensure no light would pass though. It was a very effective seal. I was plunged into absolute darkness with a total stranger. As my doubts began to rise, a faint bluish glow materialized in the middle of the room, apparently suspended in mid-air. The mist gradually resolved itself into thousands, then millions of tiny points forming a whirlpool of light floating in the darkness. I felt as though I had been transported into intergalactic space and given God's perspective on the Milky Way.

"It looks better from underneath," said the friendly voice in the darkness.

We sat on the floor on either side of the glowing apparition, with Jon's face illuminated by the soft light that seemed to be coming from the galaxy itself. We gazed along its underside, the stars billowing like the belly of a cloud. I could see the shape of the galaxy, like a fuzzy Frisbee flying through space. Its outside edges were hard to define, the stars spread thinly around the rim then clustered closer together towards the centre where they blossomed into an orange sphere at the hub of the great pinwheel.

Jon pointed to an innocuous region off to one side and said, "We live somewhere over here, although at this scale the Sun is too faint to be seen—it's lost among all the other stars."

Through a clever use of multiple layering and black lighting, Jon had brought the Milky Way to life, illustrated its tremendous size and shown a fine appreciation for its beauty. He went on to become chief artist for Carl Sagan, illustrating his books and television series.

The image of Jon's galaxy was in my mind as I gazed at the real Milky Way rising straight up out of the horizon before me in Tanzania. I was looking towards the centre of the galactic disc, a view barely visible from North America. The central bulge was clearly visible just above the horizon with the rest of the disc rising straight up from between my feet and becoming thinner as it arched directly overhead. It was easy to imagine the giant wheel slowly turning in a forward direction, as though I were straddling the rim. Our motion around the galaxy is ten times faster than the Earth's movement around the Sun so I began to feel myself being thrust forward into the void.

There was still one more perspective to add thrills to this cosmic roller-coaster ride, the perception of depth. Just off to the right of the Milky Way, two fuzzy blobs of light floated among the stars like pieces of the galaxy that had been torn off. I had never seen the Magellanic clouds before. These two small galaxies are named after Portuguese navigator Ferdinand Magellan, who first reported them when he crossed into the Southern Hemisphere during his attempt to sail around the world in the sixteenth century.

The two companion galaxies are the biggest objects visible to the naked eye that are outside our Milky Way. They hover above our giant disc like small birds chasing a Frisbee through the air. The light from those two fuzzy blobs had been travelling across space for 170,000 years just to reach my eyes. I wondered if there were any eyes out there in those distant galaxies looking back in my direction. They certainly have the better view. From above the Milky Way, they have the benefit of an overhead perspective on the entire whirlpool shape of the galaxy. Imagine seeing that in your backyard every night. Who knows, perhaps we won't need to travel far away to see ourselves; perhaps a portrait of our galaxy will arrive from space, taken by someone already living out there in those Magellanic clouds.

The sky before me was taking on a more three-dimensional form. Rather than a black dome with stars painted on the inside as our ancestors pictured it, I could see into the depths of space. From the side of the speeding ball to which I was clinging, I looked out at other planets swinging past, the stars behind them converging into the distant glow of the Milky Way, the two Magellanic clouds hovering beyond, all suspended against the blackness of the expanding universe. How much more lies hidden in that blackness?

My fingers were getting tired digging deeper into the grass.

Thinking about the size of it all can be a rather humbling experience but even though we may be small in size, we humans have one big advantage over the other life forms that inhabit this speck of dust we call a planet . . . we know our place in the universe. No other creature has a sense of the Earth as a planet and the stars as part of a great galaxy—at least we think not.

However, before we become too smug about our great cosmic understanding, there is one embarrassingly large error that is still uncorrected . . . most of the universe seems to be missing.

It's one of the great ironies of modern astronomy that despite the most powerful telescopes, satellites and other sophisticated equipment ever built to study the sky, we have been unable to detect 90 percent of the matter that forms the bulk of everything that exists. Some dark substance is lurking in the blackness between the galaxies and no one can find it. In fact, so little is known about it that astronomers don't even have a name for it. They simply call it "dark matter."

This rather large blunder of science has been pestering astronomers since the 1930s when Jan Hendrik Oort made an astounding observation. After measuring the swirling motion of the stars around the Milky Way, the Dutch astronomer found that the amount of gravity needed to keep them in their orbits was twice as much as that which is actually produced by the galaxy itself. Something invisible must be pulling on the stars. The path our Sun and all the other stars follow around the centre of the Milky Way is determined by the mass of all the stars added together. When Oort added up the mass of all the stars, there wasn't enough gravity to do the job, not by a long shot. The Milky Way should be flying apart, spewing stars into space like water drops from a lawn sprinkler, but it isn't. That means there must be something else out there that we're not seeing, a hidden mass that's providing the gravity to hold all the stars in their orderly paths around the centre of the galaxy. And there must be a lot of this dark matter in the galaxy, at least as much as the mass of all the billions of stars we do see. Oort set out to find the invisible matter and did succeed in discovering a hidden cloud of comets out beyond Pluto, now known as the Oort cloud, but they did not provide enough mass to account for the extra gravity the galaxy seemed to possess.

The problem gets worse when you look beyond the Milky Way. Galaxies travel in groups and one of the largest is the Virgo Cluster, containing about 250 large galaxies and at least a thousand lesser ones, all intimately tied together by their mutual gravity. But the amount of gravity needed to contain that group is about three hundred times more than what can be accounted for by the galaxies themselves. There's something out there holding those galaxies together; we just don't know what it is.

Plenty of theories have tried to explain the nature of dark matter. Perhaps it's made of brown dwarf stars, dim bulbs that aren't bright enough to show up in our telescopes, or space may be bathed in exotic sub-atomic particles like massive neutrinos, or maybe it's something completely new. Only one tantalizing image of dark matter has been produced, by the Canada France Hawaii Telescope in March 2000. It showed a large area of space containing 200,000 distant galaxies with long filaments of material strung between them, like pieces of gauze. The image isn't an actual photo of the dark matter itself, but it is the first to show where the material is located in space. The astronomers noticed that the light from the distant galaxies had been distorted as it passed through the dark matter on its way to Earth, the way filaments of smoke get in the way of lights in a bar. Computer models were able to construct a three-dimensional map of where the cosmic smoke is located, and indeed the universe is filled with a giant matrix of dark matter. Wherever the matter clumps together you find a galaxy, as though this fabric is the basic material that forged everything we consider reality. We may not know what that stuff is, but at least we now know where to look. A new era of astronomy is beginning where we forget about the light and peer into the nature of darkness.

As I peered into that blackness beyond the Milky Way I tried to fathom the idea that darkness is what most of the universe is made of. My feeling of insignificance grew.

The longer you look into the night sky, the more stars appear filling in the black spaces. Eyes strain from the effort to spot more faint points of light. Of course, that's why we invented telescopes, to make our eyes bigger and capture more of that distant light. It doesn't matter how big our telescopes get, there seems to be no end to the number of new stars and galaxies that come into view. The most dramatic demonstration of what remains hidden in the darkness came in 1996 when the Hubble space telescope was pointed at a small section of the sky no larger than a grain of sand held at arm's length. According to all other telescopes on the ground, there was nothing there but empty space. But after staring into the void for one hundred hours, the big eye in the sky revealed hundreds of new galaxies far out at the edge of the universe, more than ten billion light years away, almost back to the beginning of time. The galaxies that filled the image are believed to be so young they are still in the process of being born.

I tried to grasp the fact that the stars above me were ghosts from the past. The light reaching my eyes had left those stars years ago. What we see in the night sky is history, a record of past events carried to our eyes by the messenger of light. One of the consequences of living in a very large universe is that it takes time to go anywhere, even if you travel at the speed of light. Light is a slow messenger from the stars, so what we see in telescopes is not what's happening at the moment, it's what happened in the past. Telescopes are time machines.

It's like taking a photograph of yourself and sending it to a friend through the mail. By the time your friend gets it, the you in the photograph is the you from several days ago, not the you at the time they see the picture. Suppose the picture gets lost in the mail for months or years. By the time your friend gets it you have changed. There are many events taking place in the universe at this moment: exploding stars, black holes swallowing giant companions, galaxies in collision that we cannot see because the light from those events hasn't reached us yet. We cannot see the universe as it is now.

There is one advantage to this distorted view of the cosmos, though: It allows us to see our own evolution. Theoretically, if telescopes become powerful enough, we should be able to see back to the beginning of time. In fact, we almost have.

Hubble was puzzled by the nature of the expansion; the universe is not billowing outwards like glowing flares from fireworks. Material thrown out from a fireworks explosion all flies away at about the same speed. In fact, the material at the outer edge of the explosion slows down over time. Watch fireworks and you will see the effect: Brilliant flares shoot out from the bang, slow down and fall gently to Earth. That's the image that makes intuitive sense when we think of the expanding universe, but that's not what is happening. Hubble found the farther away galaxies are, the faster they seem to be moving. The only explanation was that the galaxies are not actually moving away from each other like shrapnel out of an explosion; the very fabric of space itself is expanding carrying the galaxies with it. In other words, space is stretchy like a rubber band. You can demonstrate this yourself with an elastic band. Using a ballpoint pen, make four marks all the same distance apart on the side of the band. Before it is stretched, measure the distance from the first dot to each of the others and you will find that the distance increases by the same amount each time. Then hold one end and stretch the band as far as it will go and measure the distance between the dots again. You will find that starting from one end, the distance from the first dot to the others doubles as you go along. So from the first to the second the distance is one, then two, four, until the last dot which is eight times farther away than the distance between the first two.

(Go get a rubber band right now and try it to see what I mean.) On top of that, while you are stretching the band out the dots are moving away from each other in a similar relationship: The farthest dot is moving away much faster than the other three.

That's exactly what telescopes see when they look at the most distant galaxies: their speed increases with distance which means the universe is a giant rubber balloon.

Einstein called it the curvature of space-time and physicists around the world, including Stephen Hawking, are still trying to figure out how it works. If that's not enough to twist your head, more recent measurements have shown that the expansion of space-time is speeding up. Some force, a type of anti-gravity, is pushing the universe outwards. It's been called vacuum energy or the cosmological constant but, really, no one knows exactly what that force is or how it works.

So if the universe is expanding, what is it expanding into?

The short answer a cosmologist will give is "nothing. The universe by definition is all there is, so nothing exists outside of it." Of course this idea goes completely against our common sense. We like to put things inside other things. At the supermarket, we take food that is already wrapped in plastic and put it in another bag to be carried home. A bag in a bag, in a building, in a city, in a country—everything is inside something larger. So why can't the universe be inside something bigger as well? It seems totally natural.

The cosmologists say that even if there is a larger space, we can't see it because our gaze outwards is bent back on ourselves by Einstein's idea of curved space. Look far enough in one direction and eventually you will see the back of your own head. We are trapped in a cosmic bubble.

That predicament hasn't stopped people from guessing what might be on the outside, if there is one. In 1992 the Cosmic Background Explorer satellite, affectionately known as *COBE*, was launched with the goal of peering at the farthest object known in the universe, a glow that comes from all parts of the sky called the cosmic background radiation. This extremely faint glow from beyond all the galaxies was only discovered in the 1960s and is believed to be the leftover ember from the big bang itself. That makes sense when you think about it. If the farther into space you look, the farther back in time you see, looking back ten or fifteen billion years you should see the creation of the universe. But remember, we are part of the big bang so we see it from the inside. An inside view of an explosion would show fire in all directions, which is exactly how the background radiation appears—it comes from all parts of the sky at once. The *COBE* satellite was designed to map this glow, to see if it had any texture, which would tell us about the conditions just after the moment of creation. The map from COBE showed lumps and blobs larger than anything ever seen before. The early universe was lumpy. That's not so bad considering the current universe is pretty lumpy, what with all the stars, planets and galaxies scattered about. But the lumps of the early universe were too large to have grown so big in such a short time.

The only way they could grow that large that fast was to expand faster than the speed of light, which violates the prime directive of the universe, nothing can travel faster than light (yet), or the alternative explanation, perhaps the universe did expand into something larger.

When I asked Dr. George Smoot, head of the COBE project about these lumps he suggested that perhaps what we are seeing is part of a cosmic foam. The universe that we know could be like one bubble in a tub full of soap suds. You've probably seen the effect in a bath when one bubble grows larger than all the rest, pushing the other suds out of the way. The whole sudsy structure changes because of the expansion of that one bubble.

The giant lumps detected by the COBE satellite could be part of the foam from the rest of the universe which we pushed out of the way when our bubble universe expanded. Those big structures out there didn't have to grow faster than the speed of light—they already existed beforehand. Our universe may have grown inside something larger after all. Perhaps one day we will peer out of our bubble universe into the next, or try to see who's taking a bath. On the other hand we might discover that our perception of the universe is entirely wrong. After all, we have been wrong before.

We think we're so smart with all our science and mathematics, but really, when it comes down to basics, we still don't know the answers to the most fundamental questions . . . what was the universe like in the very beginning, why did it blow up in the first place and was there anything before?

In other words, we don't know the answers to the questions every child asks, "Where did we come from? Where are we going?" Now that we know that the universe is speeding up, its ultimate fate seems to be rather dismal, just a fade to black as the stars burn out, galaxies go dark and matter doesn't matter any more. It's kind of sad really. I preferred the old theory that one day the universe will stop expanding then be pulled back in on itself by the relentless force of gravity until everything collapses into the big crunch then rebounds outwards again in a never-ending cycle of birth and death like a huge cosmic heart. But alas, it seems we are destined to fizzle out like a fireworks display that blazes briefly then turns to cinders blown on the wind.

These are the mysteries that lay spread out before me that night on a hill in Tanzania: bubble universes, the rubbery texture of space stretching outwards, galaxies held together by invisible dark matter, billions of stars gathered in the Milky Way and me stuck to the side of a little rock spinning around one of those stars. I can't say I grasped all of it but it was a privilege to even have those thoughts that night. They were gifts from great thinkers who came before me: Eratosthenes, Hubble, Lomberg, people who wouldn't accept simply what our five senses tell us about the world. It was truly a cosmic journey, the power of knowledge providing a heady experience more potent than drugs. I marvelled at how remarkable it was that I knew all that, and pondered whether any other sentient creatures on the planet have a similar grasp of the universe at large.

Go into a field
And stand on your head
Let the stars be the firmament
Upon which you tread
And hold for a moment
This strangely solid Earth
On your strangely solid head

Anonymous

RIDING THE WALLS OF THE GRAVITY WELL

A true-life adventure in deep space

———————— "IT FLOATS . . . SATURN FLOATS."

I can't believe it. I barely know what a planet is at the age of six, but here, spread across two pages in the large book before me is a beautiful beach-ball planet, its face criss-crossed by swirling brown clouds, a broad band of brilliant white rings circling its midriff as precisely as the brim of a Mountie's hat. The huge planet hangs low in the black, star-studded sky, floating just above a rocky, snow-covered horizon. I have been transported to a moon of Saturn and am awestruck. I fall right into the image of an alien world and drink in the incredible view.

Below the colourful illustration the caption reads, "From this moon, Saturn would fill half of your sky."

Astounding. I have just discovered another world.

Farther below it reads, "Saturn is the lightest planet, made mostly of gas and liquid, in fact, if you could find an ocean large enough, Saturn would float!"

Unbelievable. A floating planet . . .

I run downstairs waving the book in my hand shouting, "Mom, look, there's a planet that floats!!"

She is busy ironing laundry so all I get is, "That's nice dear, now go read somewhere else." Mothers have a remarkable ability to acknowledge their children then brush them off. Little does she know that her son's interest in space has just been imprinted for the rest of his life. Little does her son know that he will actually witness the exploration of that planet and that moon twenty-four years later.

My interest in space all began with that illustration of Saturn as seen from one of its moons in a book my mother gave me when I was a kid. The image is forever etched in my memory. The artist had transformed a flat drawing into a three-dimensional world, a place where I might go in the future and see that giant planet in the sky. At the time, artists' illustrations were better than actual photographs because the only real pictures of the planets available were fuzzy images taken through telescopes that didn't show much detail. All that would change of course with the space age, which began on October 4, 1957, the year *Sputnik* became the first robot to orbit this world, the same year I discovered Saturn in that kids' book.

I was among millions around the world who were astonished and amazed by the world's first artificial satellite. It was just an aluminum sphere, not much bigger than a basketball and equipped with a simple radio transmitter. There wasn't even a camera on it, yet that little satellite from the Soviet Union symbolized tremendous power. A country now had enough power to overcome the pull of gravity and commence our journey to other worlds.

Of course, American politicians felt very uncomfortable with all that power residing in the Soviet Union, which triggered the insane competition to reach the Moon. But it also provided an unprecedented boost to space exploration.

The front page of the Orillia *Packet and Times* was covered with a drawing of the Earth and *Sputnik* circling around it. We all rushed outside to join half the neighbourhood who had gathered in the street hoping to get a glimpse of the new spaceship.

By the time Armstrong and Aldrin made their daring first Moon landing twelve years later, robots had already been to Venus and Mars. Few people remember the robots because a spindly machine scooping up Moon dust just doesn't compare to an astronaut hitting a golf ball out of sight. The truly daring adventures of the *Apollo* astronauts captured the imagination of people everywhere because it was human drama at its best. Every step outwards was a first: the first satellite, first man in orbit, first trip to the Moon, first step, first return home, all happening live on television.

But while the human dramas of the Moon missions were exciting, the astronauts relied on road maps made by robots, which had been there first. The Sea of Tranquillity and other landing sites were photographed, surveyed by a host of robots that visited the Moon long before the humans arrived. The first footprints on the Moon were made not by Neil Armstrong in 1969, but by the mechanical feet of a Russian robot called *Luna 9* three years earlier. The first Moon rocks were picked up by a robotic scoop on *Surveyor 1* in 1966. There was even a last-minute attempt by the Soviet Union to bring Moon rocks back to Earth by robot before Armstrong and Aldrin made it home. While the Americans were planting the first flag, *Luna 15* was orbiting the Moon over their heads. The robot was supposed to make a soft landing just west of the *Apollo 11* site, snap up about one hundred grams of lunar soil and scoot back to Earth so the Soviets could say they didn't need to send men to the Moon. Unfortunately the probe crashed . . . in the Sea of Crisis.

Our first forays to other worlds have always been by robot, small machines that go where no one has gone before, including many places no human can go. Automatic probes have pierced the rings of Saturn, dived into the clouds of Jupiter, been drenched by sulphuric acid rain on Venus and touched the snows of Mars. They are the true explorers of the solar system.

It was a sweet coincidence that I happened to become a science journalist at the time when the first spacecraft were sent out to those planets. I got to see my moon of Saturn for real. The decades of the seventies and eighties have been called The Golden Age of Planetary Exploration, when a fleet of semi-intelligent robots armed with cameras and other surveillance equipment were sent out to almost every planet in the solar system. Pluto is the only exception and a mission is in the works to go there in 2002.

In the spirit of the fifteenth-century explorers, the twentieth-century craft were called *Viking, Mariner, Ranger, Voyager, Magellan* and crossed the vast distances of interplanetary space on journeys lasting months or years, about the same length as their historical namesakes. These incredible machines and the unsung heroes who built and flew them were modern-day explorers literally discovering new worlds. They saw alien horizons, surveyed and mapped strange landscapes and set their mechanical feet down on the most distant soils. During this remarkable era of pure exploration more than a dozen new moons were discovered, each a distinctive world unto itself.

And while the brave crews of *Apollo* had to endure three days confined to a spacecraft with about as much interior space as a minivan to reach the Moon, they really didn't go very far by solar system standards. In cosmic terms, the Moon is right in our backyard. If Earth were a speck of dust, the Moon would be another speck two centimetres away, about the width of your thumb. Mars would be another dust mote a metre and a half away and you would have to drive more than fifteen kilometres to get to Pluto. If Earth is an island in an ocean of space, a trip to the Moon is a short hop to another island within sight of shore. The other planets are well over the horizon. Journeys across the ocean of space to other worlds take months or years, just like the days of old, which is another reason to make the voyage by robot—they don't complain about the length of the trip.

The journey across the solar system may be long but the scenery is spectacular. There are more than fifty other moons going around other planets that are much more interesting than our own. In fact, the Moon is one of the least interesting bodies out there to explore . . . dead, no air, no liquid water, basically a lifeless world which, it appears, it has always been. It's also got one of the most boring names . . . "the." We've done such a great job of giving other moons beautiful names . . . Titania, Oberon, Ganymede, Callisto, Europa . . . So what do we call our own? "THE" Moon. What a lousy name. Perhaps it's fitting that a dull name goes to one of the dullest satellites.

Moons with more colourful names are far more colourful worlds, literally. They come in an assortment of hues including red, white and blue. Some are made entirely of ice, others are covered with erupting volcanoes; there are even moons with atmospheres and oceans, each a unique alien world, almost all far more interesting than plain old "the."

In fact, as the robotic exploration of the solar system proceeded, the moons going around other planets turned out to be the real stars of the show, more interesting than the planets themselves. "Expect the unexpected" became the motto of the planetary space program.

Whenever a robot was sent to another planet I tried to make the trek to the mecca of planetary exploration, the Jet Propulsion Laboratory in Pasadena, California.

Nestled into the foothills of the San Bernadino Mountains, this campus-like lab is where missions to the planets are designed, built and controlled. Every mission brought together a core of journalists and scientists who shared the excitement of being the first humans to set eyes on these new horizons. During one of the missions to Saturn, I was asked by Barbara Frum, who was then the host of "As It Happens" on CBC Radio, what the atmosphere was like in the room when the live pictures come in from space. I said, "Imagine a camera mounted on the mast of Columbus's ship at the moment the lookout shouts, 'Land Ho!' and you are watching it all happen on a television back in Europe."

Mind you, seeing something for the first time is a perfect setup for making mistakes when you try to interpret what you see. Some of the moons in the solar system are so bizarre the scientists were at a loss to explain what was showing up on the television monitors. The flood of pictures from space was so great that the imaging team would have to meet for hours every day and choose the few pictures that they could say a few things about and prepare presentations for the hungry press corps. Often the pictures they were passing over were just as interesting as those they chose.

Meanwhile, television monitors throughout the press room displayed black-and-white images coming down from the spacecraft in real time. Journalists are a competitive lot and we would constantly try to one-up each other with our scientific knowledge, especially when there was a scientist around so we would appear to know what we were talking about. This all came to a comical head one evening when one of the imaging team scientists wandered through the press room just as fresh live pictures of a moon of Neptune appeared on the monitors. Triton is about as far away from our moon as you can get, both in distance and form. It resides at the outer edge of the solar system, a region so cold most worlds are made of more ice than rock. Triton is one of the few moons in the solar system with an atmosphere, a snow-covered surface and geysers spewing dark clouds into the thin methane air. We know all that now, but when the first black-and-white pictures came in all we could see were strange light and dark markings all over the face of the moon. A small group of us corralled the scientist over to the monitor for a look. Like the rest of us he was seeing this moon for the first time. Immediately the journalists began throwing out their pet theories on what it was we were seeing.

"I think this dark spot is an impact feature."

"No, it looks like an albedo feature to me."

"It might be unusual relief in the topography," I chime in.

On and on we go in our little game as pseudo-scientists. The real scientist meanwhile stands quietly scratching his chin, examining the picture and not saying a word. When the guessing game of the journalists settles down all eyes turn to him.

"What do you think, doc?"

He pauses for a moment then points to a large dark smudge near the bottom of the picture. We all wait in anxious anticipation to find out which one of us is right.

He brings his finger back to his chin, pausing a little longer, then proclaims, "I think it looks like a bunny."

We all stare at him, then back to the picture and back to him again.

"A bunny?"

"Yeah, see the two ears over here and the little nose? Yup, I think it looks like a bunny."

Everyone is dumbfounded.

"That's very funny doctor, but what do you think it really is?"

"I can't tell you that because I've only been looking at this picture for thirty seconds. We have to analyze it, have meetings and decide on our interpretations and publish the data. I can't do instant science, so as far as I'm concerned, it's a bunny."

He was right. We had committed the very sin that journalists love to accuse scientists of: getting lost in the jargon and jumping to conclusions too quickly. I checked the papers the next day to see if there were any headlines reading "Bunny Found on Moon of Neptune!" but there were none. Too bad, it would have been a real attention-grabber.

When you consider how far space robots travel and how cold, dark and dangerous it is in deep space, you can't help getting attached to these little marvels that head out like mechanical pets to sniff around in hazardous environments for us while we sit comfortably at home watching the results on television. Have you ever wondered what happens to all these robots eventually?

From the beginning, the flights of the robotic spacecraft have been intended to be one-way trips. That's one of the reasons they are cheaper than sending humans: you don't have to bring them back. Each spacecraft has a "design lifetime"— the time in which it's expected to perform all the tasks assigned to it. This can range from minutes to years. *Venera 7,* the first probe to land on Venus in 1970, lasted only thirty minutes before it was baked by the searing temperatures at the surface. A probe released from the *Galileo* spacecraft parachuted into the clouds of Jupiter and lasted an hour before it was crushed by the pressure of the giant planet's atmosphere. But no matter what the expected lifetime, most probes last longer than the mission calls for. *Voyager* started out as a four-year, two-planet mission; it continued on for twelve years, passing two more planets, and is still sending back signals from beyond the solar system today.

But eventually all good missions must come to an end, and the way it's done is often like abandoning a pet. The first interplanetary probes were pretty crude, just flying cameras, with radio transmitters to send images back to Earth so there wasn't much of a loss when the mission ended. In the early days of the space program, just getting to another world was a tremendous accomplishment. But now, with the development of artificial intelligence, the robots have become more sophisticated, even smarter.

Sojourner, the six-wheeled rover that drove around on Mars in 1997, was equipped with two cameras for binocular vision, laser rangefinders so it could judge the distance of objects around it and enough smarts to go from place to place without running into things. It had the intelligence, for example, to decide whether it would be able to drive over a rock or have to navigate around it. Controllers on Earth simply told it where they wanted it to go and it figured out its own way to get there, just like a dog after a scent.

The farther away from Earth the robots get, the more self-sufficient they need to be because radio signals take many minutes or hours to travel from here to other planets and back again. The one-way light time between Earth and Mars can be up to twenty minutes. That means the robots cannot be controlled the same way radio-controlled toy cars are on Earth, because there is too much of a delay between the time the signal is sent and the time it's received. The robots need to take care of themselves, which makes them seem more like pets than machines. If you've ever lost a pet, you know the thoughts that go through your head are always the worst possible scenarios. You imagine your animal cowering in a cold, wet place, pining for the comfort of home.

I know robots can't pine, but we do abandon them and in some cases they seem to behave like lost pets. *Sojourner*, for example, was a solar-powered vehicle, so every day when the Sun came up on Mars, it would come to life and wait for instructions from Earth before beginning its day's work. *Sojourner's* link to its home planet was through its mother ship, *Pathfinder*, sitting a few metres away. Unfortunately, as the mission wore on, *Pathfinder's* battery was running low. That really wasn't a problem because the mission had already lasted longer than expected. Just before *Pathfinder* completely lost power, a command was sent to *Sojourner* to come back to home base. That was the last message that would have got through.

The rover team couldn't help wonder what happened to their little *Sojourner* after it got that message. Quite possibly, once it received the command to return to base, it began driving straight towards *Pathfinder*. But being a smart little robot, it knows it's not supposed to come too close to the mother ship. Unless it's told to do otherwise, the rover is programmed to approach to a minimum distance then circle round the mother ship until told to stop. *Sojourner* could still be wandering around in a circle on Mars today, digging a moat.

The robots that have left the solar system are an even sadder story. The computer intelligence in the two *Pioneer* and two *Voyager* spacecraft, now well beyond the orbit of Pluto, is mainly concerned with finding home. The Earth is such a small point in the sky that the spacecraft radio dishes have to be pointed very precisely, in the same way that a backyard satellite dish has to be aimed at an exact part of the sky to get proper television reception.

To make sure their antennae are pointed in the right direction, the spacecraft occasionally "phone home." When controllers back on Earth get the message from space that says "Are you still listening?" they send a reply saying "Yes" and the spacecraft continues on its merry way. If a spacecraft doesn't hear a reply, it assumes it's lost and goes into a search program to find Earth.

Like sailors of old, deep-space probes use the stars to navigate. By firing thrusters, they roll around in three different directions to find three bright stars which they use for orientation. Once they know their own position, they calculate the relative position of the Earth, point the antennae in that direction and call home again. This built-in intelligence has saved spacecraft from getting lost more than once.

The tracking stations on the ground that pick up these feeble signals from space are very expensive to operate and very busy, considering the number of other robots scattered throughout the solar system. As the probes get farther away, their signals become too weak to detect, and controllers on Earth will simply stop listening. When that happens, the spacecraft will call home, roll to find the stars, call home again, roll again on and on until they run out of manoeuvring fuel. Eventually they will tumble slowly out of control, still calling home as they wander among the stars. Who knows, perhaps someone else will pick up the call. Isn't that a familiar plot for a science-fiction movie?

The one mission that truly stands out in my mind has also been the longest so far: *Voyager*, comprising twin spacecraft sent on a twelve-year journey across the entire solar system with close flybys of Jupiter, Saturn, Uranus and Neptune along the way. This was the mission that would finally get to that little moon of Saturn from my childhood dreams.

Voyager 2 was the first to leave Earth in 1977 and I was at the launch.

A robot launch from Cape Canaveral is quite different from the launch of a space shuttle. For one thing there are far fewer people around, which makes it a much more enjoyable experience. The robots just don't grab the same public attention as an intrepid crew of astronauts parading by in orange flight suits. The other big difference is the size of the rocket. Instead of the stubby winged shuttle with bloated orange fuel tank and white booster rockets, the robots are sent aloft on slim military missiles, a shape determined during the Cold War when rockets carried warheads and had to fit through railway tunnels as they were secretly shipped around the country. The missiles are also a lot faster than the shuttle, partly because there are no people aboard, but also because they have much farther to go. The space shuttle only climbs to an altitude of a few hundred kilometres, about the distance between Toronto and Montreal, and it takes off relatively slowly. The astronauts feel a force of about three g's—or three times the force of gravity on Earth—as the shuttle makes its eight-minute climb to orbit. You can experience more g's on a looping roller coaster. The robotic probes are put through more than twenty g's during takeoff and are almost out of sight by the time the sound of the engines reaches your ears.

Jon Lomberg, a friend who had worked on the *Voyager* project, encouraged me to see the launch. Jon is an artist who specializes in astronomical subjects. He had been hired by Carl Sagan to help produce an interstellar message that would be placed on the spacecraft in case any aliens in deep space should find them. The *Voyager*s were only the third and fourth spacecraft to leave the solar system. Most robots remain within the sphere of the Sun, but those passing by Jupiter are accelerated by the powerful gravity of the largest planet, which gives them enough energy to escape the gravity of the Sun and head out among the stars of the Milky Way. *Pioneer 10* and *11* were the only other spacecraft to perform this escape manoeuvre. The *Voyager* craft were getting a quadruple kick on their flight thanks to a rare conjunction that placed all four of the giant planets in a convenient row on the same side of the sun. Astrologers and doomsayers called for great calamity, but space scientists saw it as an opportunity to skip the *Voyager*s like stones from one planet to the next, getting four worlds for the price of one mission. They called it "The Grand Tour."

Carl Sagan considered these interstellar spacecraft as emissaries from planet Earth, pieces of space junk that might one day be spotted by other space-faring civilizations living elsewhere in the galaxy. To them our robots would be unidentified flying objects. The chances of that happening are astronomically small, but deep space is a very cold, dark, empty place, which means the spacecraft will remain perfectly preserved for millions of years as they drift among the stars. So there is at least a small chance they could be found by another civilization out there among the stars.

Carl couldn't resist the opportunity to communicate with aliens no matter how dim the chances of success, so he convinced the National Aeronautics and Space Administration that a message of some kind should be included on the spacecraft to act as a greeting card for anyone who finds them. He had already managed to place engraved plaques about the size of greeting cards on the two *Pioneers* for the same purpose. The gold-anodized plaques show a diagram of a man and woman, a drawing of the Sun and nine planets and a star map to illustrate where the builders of the spacecraft are located in the galaxy. Aliens might be able to use the map to pay us a visit in the future.

The illustration of the man and the woman caused quite a stir when released to the press because the two figures wore no clothes. The purpose was to show the aliens what our bodies look like, rather than the fashion of the day. NASA was accused of sending "Smut to the Stars." I wonder if the aliens will think that.

For the *Voyager* mission, Carl wanted to send a message that would tell the extraterrestrials more about humanity than simply what we look like and where we live. Since there is no way of knowing what language the aliens speak, he chose music and pictures of Earth to represent the human race. And since it was the seventies, the message would be carried on a long-playing gold record. The disc was affectionately referred to as Earth's Greatest Hits. The space agency agreed to bolt a record onto the side of each spacecraft, but there wasn't much time for preparation because the deadline for launch was rapidly approaching.

Devising a message for an alien culture that is ignorant about Earth is no easy task. A team of advisers made up of scientists, artists and music and communication experts was quickly assembled to come up with suggestions for appropriate images and take on the enormous challenge of deciding on the music that would tell whoever finds the derelict spacecraft something about the people who built it. The advisers gathered music from across the ages and around the world. They recorded people saying hello in fifty different languages and even included whales, although no one is really sure what the whales said. Wouldn't it be interesting if the whale language was the only one the aliens understood?

The most interesting information on the record however, was the first eight minutes of the recording. Even though CDs hadn't been heard of yet, the technology to digitize pictures, or turn a photograph into a sequence of binary numbers, was just emerging. Using a special recording technology, 116 photographs and illustrations were converted into numerical information and recorded on the disc. The photographs show people doing everything from playing with children to building houses. There is a sequence of anatomical drawings of the human body showing what we look like on the inside, even diagrams of our DNA. Jon Lomberg drew several of the illustrations as well as a diagram for the cover of the album that shows how to play the disc. The package even includes a needle to play it.

On the August morning of the launch, there are surprisingly few people scattered among the wooden seats of the viewing stand. I sit among the tired advisers who have been working day and night tackling the enormous challenge of deciding which pictures and which selections from the world's music would best represent planet Earth. But after months of anguish and logistical nightmares, they have managed to pull it all together and the record has been firmly bolted to the side of the spacecraft. Now they are about to watch their cosmic message in a bottle get tossed into the unknown.

It is there, among this eclectic group of interstellar communicators that I meet Carl Sagan in person for the first time. I have been inspired by his writings and somewhat awestruck by his poetic ability to communicate science in just about any medium he chooses. On this day, however, he's quiet, probably a combination of exhaustion and a feeling of melancholy about the launch. Beside him sits his colleague Frank Drake, who has sent his own electronic message to space using the world's largest radio telescope. That radio signal is the first intentional message to another star system, different from the constant stream of electronic noise we accidentally broadcast to space through our television and radio programs. Unfortunately the target Frank chose is very far away: travelling at the speed of light, his signal will take 25,000 light years to get there. If anyone out there picks up the signal, decodes it and decides to return the call, it will take another 25,000 light years for that message to reach us. This is the problem trying to communicate with civilizations on other worlds—space is so big it takes more than a human lifetime just to get the message across. Frank is now the president of the Search for Extraterrestrial Intelligence (SETI) Institute, the organization that uses radio telescopes to listen for signs of intelligent life in the universe. Although there have been some interesting candidates, nothing has turned up so far. Then again, the universe is a big place.

From our vantage point five kilometres from the launch pad, we can just make out the silvery shape of the Titan-Centaur rocket, the most powerful military missile of the time. *Voyager* is folded neatly inside the nose cone. Jon leans over to me and says, "Boy, it sure doesn't look like a starship."

He is right. The thin candlestick harkens back to the early days of the space program when the only way to get off the Earth was atop a military rocket, which have a bad history of blowing up. The possibility of everything going up in flames adds an extra level of tension to a launch. Everyone on the *Voyager* team has worked years to get to this point, and the fruit of their labour now rests on many tons of explosive fuel that is about to be ignited.

If you haven't seen a rocket launch, try to arrange a trip to Florida around one. There really is nothing like it. Television or movie cameras don't capture the spectacle; microphones don't do justice to the sound. The anticipation of the countdown, excitement of the crowds and the unspoken possibility that tons of explosive rocket fuel could suddenly transform the entire vehicle into a ball of orange flame send a shiver up the spine that intensifies as the numbers on the countdown clock approach zero.

With seconds remaining, all eyes strain to see the first signs of motion from the distant tower shimmering five kilometres away in the Florida heat. At exactly zero, a tongue of flame erupts out of the bottom of the rocket with a brilliance seconded only by the Sun. The first "Ahh" spills from everyone's mouth. Amid billowing clouds of white smoke the needle nose of the rocket ponderously rises, balanced on its flame. Everyone holds their breath during what seems like a moment of hesitation, as though the traveller is bidding final farewell to planet Earth before departing forever. Then, after the briefest pause, it gets down to the business of climbing up into the sky.

Rockets, like cannons, give all their energy to the projectile at the beginning of the flight. The rest of the trip is spent coasting like a bullet. For an interplanetary spacecraft that means a kick in the pants from a standing start to more than

40,000 kilometres an hour in about five minutes. That kind of acceleration looks unnatural, even comical when you see it in person because nothing else accelerates like a rocket. Unlike a car or airplane that accelerates up to a top speed then holds that speed for the rest of its journey, a rocket keeps going faster and faster every second. In less than half a minute it breaks the sound barrier while still travelling almost straight up. You can feel the missile clawing its way through the air, rising on a pillar of smoke, tearing itself away from gravity's grip.

Then comes the sound, a deep, crackling roar rolling across the landscape louder than thunder. And unlike thunder, it keeps on rolling and rolling and rolling as the energy of a million horses is released from the bottom of the slender tube. The terrific noise pounds against your chest with such a deep note you feel it as much as hear it.

Everyone in the crowd gasps, some whistle, others yell. The only words that come to my lips are "Holy shit, look at that thing go!" (I admit it wasn't very poetic.)

The missile remains in sight for a little more than ten seconds before it disappears through high overhanging clouds. By six o'clock that evening it has passed the orbit of the Moon. *Apollo* astronauts took almost three days to make the same trip. *Voyager* is fast by Earthly standards but it will still take two years just to reach Jupiter, twelve years to exit the solar system, and thousands of years to even come close to another star.

As the sound of the rocket engines fades into the distance, Carl Sagan turns to the small group with tears in his eyes and says, "We sent a spaceship to the stars!"

Nothing else needs to be said.

Driving back to Cocoa Beach in the van, no one speaks much. The dream of sending something far, far away, possibly into the hands of creatures we can only imagine, has become a reality. Everyone wonders whether the message will be found, or if a finder would send a return message back. None of us will know in our lifetimes. And that is the most profound feeling, that the object we have just seen leaving Earth will outlast humanity. Ice ages will come and go, the continents will change their positions, human civilization may even vanish completely and *Voyager* will still be out there drifting silently among the stars for millions of years.

Sending spacecraft out of the solar system is no easy task, mainly because our rockets are not fast enough to escape the powerful gravity of the Sun. So planetary scientists send craft like *Voyager* on a hop and skip journey where the gravity of one planet is used to throw the spacecraft to the next, much like a game of Frisbee.

There are two secrets to a good Frisbee toss. First the thrower has to send the disc on a smooth, floating flight in the general direction of the receiver. Then a good catcher does more than just grab it out of the air and throw it back: a real Frisbee artist guides the disc around the body in a continuous motion, sending it off in a new direction with renewed energy. Believe it or not, interplanetary spaceflight is a huge game of cosmic Frisbee with the planets as the players. They call it the gravitational slingshot, and without it, spacecraft could not venture beyond Jupiter.

Using the force of gravity as a pair of hands, space scientists perform an incredibly precise game of throwing a spacecraft towards one planet so that the planet tosses it on to another with a grace that makes professional players look clumsy. The grand conjunction in the late 1970s that conveniently lined up the major planets on the same side of the

Sun provided the first opportunity to perform a quadruple hand-off, the gravitational slingshot. Without that planetary alignment, which only happens every 176 years, *Voyager*'s journey to Neptune would have taken thirty years instead of twelve.

Our solar system is simply too large for our current rockets to cross easily. Until we invent something like warp drive, people won't be able to hop between worlds like the heroes in science fiction. The gravitational slingshot is a clever way to take short cuts by stealing a little energy from the planets themselves. That's not as easy as it sounds because the planets are very far apart and all moving at different speeds around the Sun. Timing has to be within seconds on flights that take years. The lead time is enormous. Just as a Frisbee tosser aims ahead of a running catcher to a point where he hopes the two will arrive at the same time, scientists planning interplanetary flights have to aim the spacecraft at points where the planets are expected to be more than a decade in the future.

Fortunately, more than three hundred years ago Sir Isaac Newton figured out the laws of physics that determine where objects go in space. To begin the cosmic toss, the first throw is performed by a rocket, which provides enough speed to overcome the old adage that what goes up must come down. The rocket must attain a speed of at least 45,000 km/h to escape the gravity of the Earth. It usually does that in about five minutes, not a bad arm. Aiming that first toss is done by timing, the so-called "launch window" which is the precise moment when the planets are in the best position. Missing a window by a minute can cause the spacecraft to miss the target completely and in cosmic Frisbee, planets don't run madly off in all directions to catch wayward spacecraft the way a friend scrambles to save your bad toss.

Once the spacecraft has been thrown away from the Earth, it coasts on its own momentum like a bullet from a rifle. Small thrusters are able to make minor corrections in the aim about halfway through the flight, but basically the spacecraft depends on the laws of gravity set out by Isaac Newton three centuries ago.

If the aim is true, the gravity of the second planet will reach out like a hand to capture the object and pull it in. Once it arrives at the new planet, there are three options. Like a Frisbee that is simply caught and held onto, a spacecraft can head straight into the planet and hit the surface. The first robots to reach the Moon were sent on kamikaze missions where they took pictures all the way down to the moment before they were obliterated by the impact.

Since then, we've refined that somewhat. Now we try to slow them down before they hit the surface so they can survive the landing. *Pathfinder,* which flew to Mars in 1997, went straight to the surface using a combination of aeroshell, parachute and giant airbags to protect it during the bouncy landing. After a journey of more than 100 million kilometres, *Pathfinder* landed within one kilometre of its target. Good shot, good catch.

Sometimes a Frisbee receiver keeps the disc spinning a little longer by balancing it on a finger or "popping it back" into the air. That's option number two for a spacecraft. Instead of hitting the planet, it is captured by the gravity and swung into orbit. This usually means slowing down to orbital speed which can be done with yet another clever technique called aerobraking. When something skips off the top of the atmosphere, air friction acts like a brake to slow the craft down, sort of like grazing your friend's hair with the Frisbee. The *Mars Global Surveyor* performed that manoeuvre, and is now in orbit around the red planet.

The final option, the one followed by *Voyager*, is when the planet you have arrived at is not your final target, so instead of orbiting or landing, the spacecraft swings around behind the planet where it gains so much speed it is flung off in a new direction, like a Frisbee player who catches the disc then swings it around the body in one smooth motion sending it off to another player without stopping. That's the slingshot.

Planets are all moving as they orbit around the Sun and that speed is added to the speed of the spacecraft, providing a substantial boost. *Voyager*'s swing past Jupiter gave it an increase in speed of 57,450 km/h. At the same time Jupiter lost some energy but because of its enormous size, the giant planet didn't feel the loss any more than a speeding car feels a bee hitting the windshield.

Another way to think of this is to imagine a circus act where a motorcyclist rides around the walls of a large circular room. As he gains speed, he is able to ride up on the walls and stay there as long as he doesn't slow down. Too slow and he crashes to the floor, too fast and he flies off over the top of the wall. Of course the daredevil riders come as close to the limit as possible, much to the thrill of the young crowd.

Planets and stars are surrounded by gravity wells that have a similar effect on speeding spacecraft. According to Einstein, space curves around a dense object like the surface of a waterbed curving downwards around a heavy object placed in the centre. Spacecraft are able to ride the walls of the gravity well, and as in the case of the motorcyclist, speed and position are all-important. If the spacecraft approaches just fast enough it will stick to the walls and be in orbit around the planet. Too fast and it will be flung over the top, back into interplanetary space. If the speed and aim are just right the gravitational slingshot manoeuvre sends the spacecraft on a path that dips low around the wall on the backside of the planet, just barely missing the floor, which is the surface of the planet itself. Then it rides back up over the top on the far side, heading off in a new direction at a higher speed. The closer it comes to the planet, the sharper the turn. That's how spacecraft are steered through the solar system. Mission planners calculate exactly how close to a planet the spacecraft need to go and how fast they enter so the craft is tossed to the next planet.

When *Voyager 2* arrived at Uranus in 1989, twelve years after leaving Earth, it was only two minutes late, not bad after riding the gravity wells of Jupiter, Saturn and Neptune to get there. That's the equivalent of firing a rifle in Hawaii, and having the bullet bounce off a bull's eye in Vancouver then hit a second bull's eye in Regina, a third in Toronto and a fourth in Halifax.

Now that the two *Voyagers* and the two *Pioneers* are leaving the solar system, the question is, who will make the next toss? We'll have to wait about ten thousand years to find out if anyone out there is up for a game.

The gravitational slingshot is still a big part of space flight between the planets, partly because of the limitations of the space shuttle. As part of a cost-saving plan, the planetary scientists were told to switch from the powerful military rockets to the space shuttle. It sounds like a sensible idea, except that the shuttle can only reach Earth's orbit. An extra booster engine is needed to kick the probe on to another planet. When it came time to launch the *Galileo* probe to Jupiter, the cargo bay of the shuttle was too small to accommodate both the spacecraft and its booster. That meant a smaller engine was fitted to *Galileo*, which was not powerful enough to make the trip directly. But thanks to their experience riding the gravity wells of the planets, the scientists compensated for the shortfall by literally going around the block to get next door. The spacecraft was first sent in exactly the opposite direction towards Venus. Once away from the Earth it was essentially a downhill trip to our sister planet—sliding down the huge gravity well of the Sun. It then used a slingshot from Venus to boomerang back towards the Earth, which gave it a second kick. But even that wasn't enough. Like the Mighty Casey winding up for a big pitch in the classic American poem, the spacecraft headed back to Venus again, back to Earth and even past the Moon to finally get enough speed to make it to Jupiter. It was an amazing demonstration of precision flying and it saved a lot of fuel, but the scientists had to wait six years for *Galileo* to complete its roundabout journey. *Voyager*'s direct flight would have taken two. Even now, as *Galileo* orbits Jupiter, it uses the gravity of Jupiter's moons to adjust its orbit.

Despite the intricacies of aiming, the people at NASA have rarely missed, which makes them, as far as we know, the best shot in the universe. One error happened in 1999 when a mix-up in computer programming sent the *Mars Climate Observer* plunging into the red planet when it was supposed to orbit around it. The path of the spacecraft was off by only ninety kilometres, but that was enough to send it too close to the Martian atmosphere where it was slowed down by air friction and either burned up or crashed. No one knows because it all happened on the far side of the planet. Everything looked fine as the spacecraft approached Mars, fired its engine to slow down and be captured by the Martian gravity, then disappeared over the horizon. It didn't appear again on the other side.

The flight team was stunned by the loss because there was no indication that anything was wrong. An investigation revealed a mix-up between the NASA scientists and the private contractor that built the spacecraft. One used metric units to calculate the thrust of the engine; the other used imperial. Foot-pounds are different from Newton-metres so the engine burned a few seconds longer than it should have. That's how little it takes to make a difference between a successful mission and disaster.

Less than a year later the *Mars Polar Lander* was lost as it attempted to make a soft landing near the South Polar ice cap. That was a real heartbreaker because everyone was extremely cautious, checking to make sure that there were no metric mix-ups. On landing day the spacecraft entered the Martian atmosphere at exactly the right angle and speed and in apparently good health, yet it was never heard from again. The most popular theory at the time was that the Martians were shooting our spacecraft down. It's since been pinned down to a false signal that shut down the engines prematurely.

Hitting planets unintentionally casts doubt in the minds of the public over the safety of these robots, especially when they use the Earth for a gravitational assist. Some robotic craft are powered by radioisotope thermoelectric generators, which have weapons-grade plutonium at the core. During the launch of *Cassini,* a Saturn probe, protesters declared that an explosion at launch could spread plutonium all over Florida.

In fact, an explosion on the launch pad or even in the air would spread no plutonium at all. The canisters are designed and tested to withstand much greater forces than an exploding rocket. They even had the opportunity to prove that when a military rocket blew up just after a launch from Vandenberg Air Force Base in California. Technicians sifted through the rubble and found the coffee-can-sized generators completely intact and in such good condition that they were used again on another flight.

A spacecraft hitting the Earth during a flyby is another matter. The speeds are so great than an impact on land could cause an explosion powerful enough to spread plutonium into the air. The scientists say the chances of that happening are extremely small because most of the Earth is covered in water, which would dampen the impact, and because of the fact that it's more difficult to hit the Earth than to miss it. Still, there was a quiet sigh of relief in July of 1999 when *Cassini* flew to within a thousand kilometres of Earth then continued on its way to Saturn without incident. The public fear remains.

Throughout the late seventies these camera-carrying probes revealed planet after planet and the myriad of moons in fascinating detail, but I was most anxious for first contact with Saturn. I had to wait until 1980 for *Voyager*'s sophisticated cameras to zoom in on my favourite moon, which I now knew had the name Mimas.

Returning to the Jet Propulsion Laboratory for the Saturn encounter was something like a high school reunion. Thousands of journalists and scientists from around the world gathered to watch the live pictures come in from deep space, a kind of space club except this club is literally out of this world. Most of the excitement was knowing that we would be the first humans to lay eyes on these other worlds.

As *Voyager* raced through the Saturn system, I waited anxiously for its close encounter with Mimas, and I was not disappointed.

Mimas turned out to be a small ice moon that has been hit so hard there is a giant circular chip missing out of its side.

There were jokes that we had discovered Darth Vader's "Death Star" from the movie *Star Wars*. There was enough detail in the picture to see that it was a rugged landscape with towering ice cliffs, ridges and scenery unlike any found on Earth.

The strange part of this experience is that the actual picture of the moon, as interesting as it was, didn't capture the feeling of being there as well as that artist who illustrated my kid's book two decades earlier. *Voyager* didn't land on Mimas; it only took pictures from a distance as it flew by. So it never got the perspective of seeing Saturn in the sky above the horizon. Until we get a camera down onto the surface of that icy moon, we still need the hand of an artist to place us in the landscape. Thanks to the pictures taken by *Voyager*, modern paintings will be more accurate than the one that inspired me as a child. Perhaps more realistic artwork will inspire today's young people, who may actually have the opportunity to visit that distant moon and see the place of my childhood dreams with their own eyes.

Of course the one scientist who did take us down to the surface of these moons was Carl Sagan, who always made sure that he was included as a member of *Voyager*'s science team.

Planet Earth lost a great citizen the day Carl Sagan died. If the message he sent aboard *Voyager* is ever found in the distant future by another space-faring race, perhaps they will get a glimpse into the spirit of a man who encouraged people on a small planet to reach out and touch other worlds.

Carl's death also underlined how long it takes to reach those other worlds—in his case, more than a lifetime. Each time our intrepid team of scientists and journalists got together for an encounter with another planet we saw the landscapes of our faces changing. We were all watching each other grow older. When *Voyager 2* lifted off Cape Canaveral in

1977, I was there as a long-haired motorcycle rider. By the time it reached Neptune twelve years later, my hair was considerably shorter and turning grey. Many scientists working on that mission lost their hair altogether. Our current method of travelling in space is agonizingly slow. We are a long way from being able to skip from planet to planet as easily as going for a Sunday drive.

It has been an extreme privilege to be alive and working as a science journalist during the first missions to the Moon and the planets. The excitement and spirit of exploration is at its height when you go somewhere for the first time, a thrill knowing you are among the first to see a new world. We discovered the other worlds that surround us, fascinating places, different from our own, yet members of the same planetary family.

As anyone who travels to other countries knows, you learn a lot about the foreign land but you also get a big lesson about the value of what you left behind. While the other planets and moons are truly amazing places, alien and wonderful in their own right, there is literally no place like home.

Everyone who works in the space business has developed a greater appreciation for the planet we call Earth. No matter how many new worlds come into view, the one we will always think about most is the one we came from. The Earth is not the biggest planet, it doesn't have the tallest mountains or the deepest valleys and even the clouds are larger on other worlds. But while all those other places are interesting to visit, none of them is easy to live on. Take a walk on Venus and you will choke, gasping for oxygen in a carbon-dioxide atmosphere. As you lie on the ground gasping, your body will begin to cook on the sizzling rocks heated to 450 degrees

Celsius by a runaway greenhouse effect, then you will be crushed by the pressure of the dense air and finally watch your flesh dissolve away due to the sulphuric-acid clouds.

Step outside on Mars and you will choke in the thin carbon-dioxide atmosphere. As you lie gasping, frostbite burns from temperatures as low as –100°C will turn you into frozen meat in less than an hour. Go anywhere near Jupiter and you will be bathed in radiation more powerful than a chest x-ray, until you suffer through the slow agonizing death of radiation poisoning. The planets beyond Jupiter are cold, forbidding worlds where humans cannot survive without an enormous amount of technology. Even Mimas, my moon of Saturn with the great view, would be a cold, difficult place to live. Scorching heat, freezing cold, lethal radiation . . . there is nowhere in the solar system other than on Earth where humans can live easily.

There has been talk of "Terra-forming" the planets, seeding Mars with hardy bacteria that would inject oxygen into its atmosphere, sprinkle dust over its ice caps so they heat up, release water vapour into the air so rain, rivers and lakes can once again flow, turning the red planet into a blue one. Technically it could be done but the cost would be enormous. Besides, is it really our place to be changing the environments of planets? We're not doing a very good job of managing the environment of the one we live on. Still, ours is the only planet we know of where social convention alone might prevent you from stepping outside and breathing the fresh air, wearing nothing more than a bathing suit. It's no accident that within a year of the first whole Earth pictures being taken from the Moon, the first Earth Day was celebrated and the U.S. Environmental Agency, Environment Canada and Greenpeace were formed. The environmental movement was born when we finally saw ourselves in our true context, a small blue island of comfort in a very large, black, cold, empty space.

The last picture of the whole Earth taken by a hand-held camera was taken by Harrison Schmitt, a member of *Apollo 17*, the last mission to the Moon. He was also the only scientist to go there. That picture, showing the full Earth with Africa in the centre and the white polar ice cap of Antarctica framing the bottom, has become the symbol of the environmental movement, showing up on posters everywhere. But to me, the symbology goes beyond just seeing ourselves from the outside. It is also looking back to our own origins. In the very centre of that photograph is East Africa, where some of the oldest remains of our human ancestors have been found. According to the latest theories of anthropology, everyone on the face of the Earth today who call themselves human beings had their origins in that part of the world, the part exactly in the centre of the last photograph from space. How appropriate. In three million years a species learned how to walk upright, make tools, develop technology, fly and leave the planet. We have seen amazing faraway places, but more importantly we have seen ourselves from afar. And what we see is rare, precious and most beautiful.

When future historians look back on this remarkable period of human evolution we will probably be remembered as the explorers, the wandering tribes who discovered planet Earth. As we face a new millennium we are still ignorant about the nature of our planet. Yes, we have mapped it from pole to pole, but the new challenge is to understand the Earth in a dynamic sense.

I think of the Earth as an onion, made of many thin layers one inside the other. On the outside is the atmosphere, the thin film of gas that enshrouds the planet with a thickness that by comparison is less than the fuzz on a peach. Originally a

poisonous mixture of methane and ammonia, the exotic cocktail of gases that make up this thin veil are constantly mixing
and chemically interacting with each other. Plants remove
carbon dioxide and contribute oxygen. Sunlight breaks down
oxygen forming it into ozone, heat rises from the surface and
is carried towards the poles in a never-ending battle of energy
that tosses thunderstorms and hurricanes around the globe.
We know that the new additions to this chemical brew, gases
from our industry and automobiles, are changing the dynamics
of the atmosphere. Every year of the nineties was a record
breaker for temperature, but predicting how much the atmosphere will change and how quickly that will happen is
extremely difficult. Remember, weather can be predicted only
five days in advance and even that's unreliable.

Beneath the atmosphere is the hydrosphere, an even thinner
film of water that almost surrounds the planet. El Niños, coral
bleaching, harmful algal blooms and the collapse of fish stocks
continue to surprise us every year. Under the water is the
geosphere, the main body of the Earth which rumbles, shakes
and belches through earthquakes and volcanoes. No one can
predict with certainty when the next big one will happen.

Our knowledge of the dynamic Earth is almost as short-
sighted as the image of the planet was to early explorers.
Understanding how the planet does what it does is the first
clue to how we can live with it in a sustainable way. That's
assuming that we will include ourselves as part of the system.
It's easy to become despondent over our ignorance but I actually have faith in our ability to adapt to changing environments. After all, that is the reason we have survived this long
in our evolution. Animals and even other species of humans
have not been able to cope with environmental stress; *Homo
sapiens* has. The real question is whether we can live with the
environment of the future.

A key reminder of our place in this living organism called planet Earth will always be the view of home from space. I have a short movie that I show at the end of every public presentation called simply *Earth Rotation Movie*. It is unique— the first film ever to show the Earth performing one of its most fundamental dynamic actions . . . turning. The film was made in 1991 when the *Galileo* spacecraft was sent on a long looping trajectory towards Venus then back to the Earth. This was the first opportunity to see a fully lit Earth for long enough to take a series of pictures over a twenty-four hour period. It is only from a distant perspective that you can see the Earth move. Astronauts on the space shuttle are too close to the planet to see it turning and those who went to the Moon had better things to do with their time than stare at the Earth for twenty-four hours. Even weather satellites don't see it turn because they are positioned in high geostationary orbits that keep the satellite permanently over one spot on the ground. *Galileo* was far enough away for a long enough period to record this simply elegant film of the Earth turning once while suspended in the blackness. Whenever I show it to audiences I have to emphasize that it is not computer anima-tion, it's the real thing. The room becomes silent as I show the film. I can feel the emotion building as everyone sees how beautiful and rare the planet really is. I see even more powerful emotion on the faces of people who have left the Earth and seen that beauty in its full glory.

A Taste of the Right Stuff

*The secret ingredient that gives
you lift-off potential*

So there I was, walking through Moscow's Red Square talking to a Canadian jet-fighter pilot, now an astronaut about to fly on an American space shuttle that would link up with a Russian space station. When I connected with the irony of this moment, the astronaut, Chris Hadfield, gave a wry smile.

"Yeah, especially since I've had Russian MiGs in the gunsights of my F-18."

Chris was in Moscow training for his flight aboard the *Mir* space station and I was there preparing a television documentary on his flight for "The National." It was a rare opportunity to witness the determination of modern-day adventurers who have whatever stuff it takes to leave the planet and come back to tell about it. Chris Hadfield knew when he was a kid that the only way a Canadian could become an astronaut was to first learn to fly fighter jets then become a test pilot, just like the American heroes that he watched walk on the Moon.

And fly he did, piloting the fastest Canadian jets, on to the United States Air Force test pilot school where he graduated with top honours, then repeating the honours with the U.S. Navy. Finally, as a member of the Canadian astronaut corps he was about to ride the shuttle up to the Russian *Mir* space station on his very first mission into space. Yes, he really is a "Right Stuff" kind of guy: lean, fit, focused, his eyes as steady as a cat about to pounce on its next prey.

As we strolled through Red Square, framed by St. Basil's Cathedral and Lenin's tomb, I tried to understand exactly what is meant by "Right Stuff," a term coined by author Tom Wolfe, who used it to describe the daredevil character of the first astronauts in the early days of the space program. I've seen that stuff in all the astronauts I've met, but it's hard to describe, a focused determination that drives them to be the absolute best then push a little beyond that. Such perfection in performance is rare in today's convenience-filled workplace.

The daredevil inspiration for Tom Wolfe was Chuck Yeager, the original Mr. Right Stuff immortalized in the history books as the first man to break the sound barrier. I had the opportunity to meet him backstage while we were both waiting to go on air. He had just released his biography, *The Real Stuff,* which told the true tale of his career as an air force test pilot without all the hype created by Tom Wolfe's account. He was a pilot at heart who chose to remain with aircraft rather than spacecraft. He considered the small capsules used on the first missions as bullets not airplanes. They didn't have wings and the pilot had little control. Any monkey could do that, and did. To Chuck Yeager, astronauts were "Spam in the can."

In retirement he was still qualified to fly supersonic high-performance aircraft, a task usually reserved for people half his age.

I knew that he had already faced the obvious questions, about what it was like to break the sound barrier (nothing like the movie) and why he didn't become an astronaut, a million times during his book tour. As I approached to say hello I could see him mentally preparing for another boring question. I tried to think of something different.

"What do you think of the new flyby wire systems, where computers are now flying the airplanes and the pilot just operates a joystick?"

Immediately his eyes lit up, his posture changed and he burst into a long dissertation on the benefits of electronic control. "Today's aircraft are far more capable than anything in my day. Boy, you point the nose of that baby at the horizon, snap the stick into a 360-degree roll, snap it level again and that nose is still pointed right at the horizon . . . ."

I had obviously scored. It was a joy to spend a few minutes with a legend talking about his favourite subject. Throughout our conversation I tried to figure out what it was that made this guy a little different, but it basically came down to a childlike joy of flying. Perhaps the same fearlessness that children have when they ride their bikes with no hands or climb up dangerous heights stays with some people throughout their lives.

A glimmer of that Chuck Yeager grin played across the face of Chris Hadfield as we walked through Red Square. There is something about exploring the edge of human ability that changes people. Every astronaut I've met before and after their flight in space is different when they return. There's a look about them, something sort of like knowing when someone just lost their virginity. It's a look hard to describe, but you can see it. That's not too surprising really, after all space flight affects people in more ways than one: It puts their bodies through strange forces, alters their sense of up and down and certainly improves their perception of their home planet.

As a journalist I've had the opportunity to get a very tiny taste of what it takes to be one of these people and see if any of that right stuff is running through my veins. While I haven't faced the ultimate test of flying space, I've been tumbled end over end, spun and whirled around in some of the same equipment used to train astronauts. If nothing else, I've gained a much better appreciation of how gruelling space flight can be and what remarkable people it takes to endure it.

One of the more unpleasant aspects of space flight, the one astronauts don't like to talk about, is motion sickness. It's been a chronic problem throughout the space program, affecting about half of all the people who have flown in space. Medications to fight motion sickness have been developed but some people are reluctant to take them, believing it will dull their reaction time. The strange part of it is that there is no correlation between the people who become sick training on the ground and those who become sick in space. The best way to deal with it is to spend time in acrobatic aircraft or clever torture devices on the ground that are designed to help you recognize the symptoms long before you lose your lunch.

Dr. Ken Money, one of Canada's first astronauts and a leading expert on motion sickness, offered to take me for a ride in one of these sadistic machines called the PAM. The name stands for Primary Axis Mover, which means it can spin you in any direction and at any speed. Dr. Money tumbled me in only one direction, at one speed for five minutes.

The PAM is part of the testing equipment at the Defence and Civil Institute for Environmental Medicine in Toronto, where studies are done on pilots and astronauts. The device looks like a large black drum with a big motorized arm sticking out of its side. The arm spins the drum with a very smooth action. A small door in the front of the contraption is just large enough to allow me to wedge myself into the single chair inside. It feels like crawling into an old pot-bellied stove. After the five-point seat belt is securely tightened around my thighs and shoulders the door is closed in front of my face. I feel suddenly trapped and alone in a very confined space with no windows. My head is held fast by head-rests that also serve as an intercom to Dr. Money. With nothing but a single dim lamp to illuminate the interior, I'm completely at the mercy of this machine. I also have faith in science and know they will take care of me.

"Are you ready?" Dr. Money chimes over the headphones.

"Ready." There really isn't much choice in the matter.

"Which direction are you going to spin me?" I ask, trying to sound calm.

"I'm not telling you that." I detect a smirk in his voice.

Since I can't see outside, I will have to rely on feeling to figure out which way I am moving.

With a silent smooth action, the machine begins tumbling forward end over end. It doesn't take long to figure out which way I'm moving. My body presses forward against the harness as I turn upside down, then sinks back against the seat again as I turn back upright. The cycling continues smoothly up to a steady speed of 30 rpm. That's one tumble every two seconds.

Now, I'm a big fan of looping roller coasters and other amusement rides, especially those that turn you upside down. But this ride is a completely different experience. Roller coasters turn you in as many different directions in as short a time as possible, so in the end you feel a little disoriented but it passes in a few seconds after you step off. This machine tumbles me in one direction at a constant speed for five minutes.

"How are you feeling?" comes the inquiry through the headphones.

"Just fine . . . A-OK and all that."

Inside the small capsule, I really don't want to get sick all over his fancy equipment even though I have been set up to do exactly that. I feel the end-over-end tumbling motion with my body, but with the door closed in front of my face my eyes see no motion at all. The machine does a very effective job of confusing the senses. My stomach begins to protest. At least I had the foresight to avoid breakfast so there will be little to clean up if I do spew, but that's not an option in my mind.

Almost as though he knows what I am thinking or more likely, since he has taken many rides in the thing himself, Dr. Money says, "It helps if you concentrate on the picture in front of you." He is right; a photograph taped to the inside of the door provides a subject to focus on. (I think it was Miss October. This was, after all, a military institution.) But as interesting as the picture is to look at, I have difficulty keeping it still. The picture constantly moves up and down every two seconds. Actually it's my eyeballs moving up and down in my head as I continue to tumble around.

After a minute or two my stomach begins to settle down so I can relax and enjoy this unusual situation. I'm in a quiet, comfortable space which, other than the constant movement of my body against the seat belts, provides very few clues to my position. In fact, I begin to lose track of when I'm upside down and when I'm right side up. It really doesn't matter anyway because my body is strapped in so tightly there is no way I can fall out. Eventually it gets to the point where I have to think, "Let's see, when I'm against the shoulder straps I'm on my head and when I feel the bottom of the seat I'm upright . . ." My position changes so fast, it's hard to keep track; besides, it makes me sick to think about it. I give up trying to keep track of my body position.

I am more comfortable enjoying the ride and getting a really good back massage with all that motion against the seat. My brain is adjusting to the new reality of a world where up and down do not exist.

It's amazing how many ways we have of knowing where up and down are, considering the brain is locked inside a thick dark skull. Like a kidnap victim trapped in the trunk of a speeding car, the brain uses every bit of information available to know where it is. If details are missing, the brain relies on whatever is left over, and that's what was happening to me in the PAM.

The brain has three basic ways of determining up and down: the eyes, organs of balance in the ears and pressure cues coming from the body. In my state of constant tumbling end over end in the PAM, the information coming from those different sources didn't agree, which was totally disorienting and a perfect setup for motion sickness. There were no windows in the capsule so my eyes saw no spinning at all while my body was detecting the real fact that I was being stood on my head and back upright every two seconds. Not knowing which was true, my brain began to lose faith in where up and down really were. It withdrew from the real world and created its own reality. I began to feel like I was floating motionless while up and down slowly dissolved.

Losing your sense of up and down, or vertigo, hits pilots, astronauts and scuba divers. Pilots flying into clouds or over the sea at night can lose sight of the horizon and all visual references for up and down. They may not realize the plane is turning or even inverted. Trying to pull "up" can actually point the plane towards the ground, a situation many pilots such as John F. Kennedy Jr. have not survived.

Divers occasionally experience the same thing in deep water when the surface is not visible. Suspended in a sea of green they sometimes get so turned around they have to stop and watch their bubbles to see which way is up. Fortunately bubbles never suffer vertigo.

When our eyes see no motion, but the body feels it, the brain relies on other cues to figure out where it is. The second most powerful signals after the eyes come from your organs of balance located in your ears. They are triggered whenever you move your head as well as by general walking and running movements. Like the compass on a ship, these organs tell your brain how your body's position is changing with respect to up and down.

The PAM was doing an effective job of tricking these organs as well. Attached to our inner ears are ingenious little tubes that act something like gyrocompasses, telling the brain which way our head is pointed. The semicircular canals look like little drinking straws that have been bent into an almost complete circle. The tubes are filled with fluid, which is free to slosh around whenever we move our heads. Nerve endings on the inside of the tubes detect the motion of the sloshing fluid and send a signal off to the brain that something is happening. The tubes come in a set of three, and each one is facing a different direction. One tube is standing upright, one is facing sideways and the third is lying on its side. These positions represent the three axes of motion, what pilots call roll, pitch and yaw. In other words, the tube standing straight up in line with the front of your face is positioned so its fluids move when you nod your head up and down saying yes. The tube facing sideways detects the rolling motion of your head, when your ears approach your shoulders and you say, "I don't know." The third tube, lying flat on its side detects the shaking motion when you say no.

Of course, the complex movements of daily life or a quick ride on a roller coaster keep all three canals pretty busy. As good as the system is, the semicircular canals can be easily fooled. First of all, they are designed to detect only a change in motion, a start, stop or turn. When a motion is steady, the semicircular canals stop sending signals because the fluids catch up to the motion of your head. If you start spinning yourself around like a figure skater, the canal lying on its side will sense the beginning of the spin because the fluids lag behind the motion of the head. But soon the fluids catch up to the spinning motion. Then, when you suddenly stop, the fluids continue spinning for a few seconds sending a very powerful signal to the brain that there is motion in the opposite direction. But the eyes see no motion at all. The conflict between what the eyes see and what the semicircular canals feel creates the dizzy feeling.

Another way to fool the canals is to tilt your head back while you are spinning around. The semicircular canals work independently, so if you are spinning around with your head level to the ground, only one canal is affected. When you look up while spinning, another canal is activated. That axis usually detects a tilt of the head to one side, but again that's not what's really happening—you're actually looking up. The canal was fooled because it didn't know you were already spinning. The result is that you stumble sideways. It's a great party game to have someone spin around while looking at the floor, then while still spinning, look at the ceiling. Guaranteed to make them fall over.

The next time you watch figure-skating championships, notice how many times the position of the head changes during a spin. The athletes are showing much more than an ability to perform a manoeuvre flawlessly; they are managing to triumph over dizziness from powerful false signals coming from their semicircular canals.

Pilots face a similar situation when performing acrobatics.

They try not to turn their heads during loops and spins. It's an almost guaranteed way to instantly throw up.

In space the influence of gravity is taken away altogether so the fluids in the semicircular canals are free to slosh at any time. On top of that, astronauts don't walk, they fly through the air, twisting and turning along the way involving much more complex motions of the head. On Earth we tend to keep our heads level most of the time.

All first-timers in space are advised to keep head motions to a minimum during the first day until the brain adapts to the new conditions. That's the incredible part of human orientation: The brain can be taught to accept a new set of rules.

Strapped into the PAM with my head held firmly in one position, tumbling smoothly and steadily end over end in the forward direction, I begin to lose the sensation of tumbling. The fluids in my semicircular canals are catching up to my spin. No matter how hard I try, it becomes more and more difficult to believe I'm rolling around like a lottery drum. With the door closed my eyes see no motion and my ears detect no change in speed or direction. My sense of up and down is totally fooled so my brain begins to create its own reality. I feel like I've stopped tumbling altogether and am now lying on my back looking up at the ceiling while sliding back and forth along the direction of my spine. The effect is so powerful I ask Dr. Money if he has changed the motion of the machine. He reassures me that everything is still the same.

I tell him about my illusion of facing upwards and he says that's a very common sensation—they call it the Ferris Wheel effect but haven't quite figured it out yet.

When the eyes and organs of balance are not reliable, the brain still has another source of clues for the direction of gravity. If you are sitting at this moment, thousands of pressure sensors in your skin are sending signals to your brain telling it what parts of your body are in contact with the Earth. Lots of signals are coming from the lower part of your body but few from the top of your head, unless you happen to be standing on your head at the moment. Pressure cues are coming from whatever parts of you are making contact with the chair. Perhaps the undersides of your arms and elbows are feeling the desk you're leaning on, while your fingertips feel the weight of this book pulling down towards the floor. Your brain compares all these signals to decide whether your body is standing upright, sitting or lying down. But that alone is not enough. Of course these senses can be fooled as well. If your shoulder is feeling pressure does that mean you are lying on your side, or leaning against a wall? The pressure is usually greater when you're lying down because of your weight. Aha! Another clue.

The expression "flying by the seat of your pants" is really true. Pressure on the body is one way pilots know how a plane is moving, whether it's turning, climbing or diving. One pilot actually injected Novocaine, the local anesthetic used by dentists, into his rear end and found it much more difficult to fly a plane. The things some people will do for science

In the PAM, all these clues are useless because the pressure on my body is changing constantly between the seat and the safety harness. One by one, my brain is ignoring all my senses. For all I know, the pod I am sitting in could have been sent off to Jupiter; there really is no way to tell.

After five minutes of the unusual body massage I'm informed that we are coming to a stop. Too bad, I could go on longer. As soon as the machine begins to slow down, a whole new set of strange sensations washes over me as the fluids in my semicircular canals detect the change in motion. They had already caught up to my tumbling and were turning along with me at the same speed, but as I slow down, the fluids begin spinning faster than my head, like a drink that continues spinning after you stop swirling the glass.

Under normal conditions a signal like that would tell the brain the head is tilting backwards. Since by this time my brain is convinced that I'm not spinning at all, it takes the cue from the organ of balance as the truth and I get the immediate sensation of being rolled back in the opposite direction. The deceleration of the PAM pushes me forward in the seat, another clue that would be the same if I were tumbling backwards. My brain has no information to suggest otherwise, so the powerful sensation of spinning backwards faster and faster builds with every second while in reality, I'm slowing down.

By the time I hear Dr. Money say, "OK, we're almost stopped now," I don't believe him. I'm convinced the machine is whizzing around at a dizzying pace definitely out of control. I'm about to be flung across the room amid exploding debris, the first journalist killed in a science experiment. Just then the door to the capsule opens and my brain reels at the sight of a room completely still. How could that be, I'm tumbling ass over teakettle, why is nothing spinning around? Is the whole world turning around with me?

I grapple with the realization that the world is not the way I thought it should be. All my senses tell me I'm still moving yet I see a room with people calmly walking around. The grinning face of Dr. Money appears directly in front of me. He is standing firmly on the floor even though the entire room is spinning madly. Somehow he isn't falling down.

The final, and probably most relied-upon clue the brain depends on comes from experience. It may seem obvious, but we have learned that grass is down, sky is up, the leaves of trees are above the trunk and doors are below roofs. We orient ourselves to up and down by simply looking at the world and seeing what's up. We then compare that to our personal up, the top of our head, and see how they agree.

"How do you feel?" he asks.

At first I didn't know how to answer that question because I am experiencing one of the most bizarre moments of my life. I have to just sit and stare for a few seconds while my brain accepts the new reality. It's like waking from a dream and realizing that you're not really flying. Thankfully it takes a few minutes to undo all the seat belts so there is time for the fluids in my semicircular canals to stop spinning and my brain to adjust to the real world. Even so, my first few steps are very tentative as though I have to test the floor to make sure it's not really moving.

A confused brain sees the world as a very strange place. It makes you realize that what we see every day is only one interpretation of reality.

The PAM was the first of a series of bizarre devices I would ride over the years, all designed to create the unusual experiences astronauts encounter when bodies become weightless and the sense of up and down no longer has meaning.

A few years later in another lab at York University, I was placed in two other vertigo-inducing machines that confuse the brain through a technique opposite to that of the PAM. I sat still while the room spun around me. Dr. Ian Howard has devised ways to create a conflict between what the eyes see and what the body feels, but in his case, the body doesn't move, the environment does. I sat in a chair that was suspended in the centre of a large white sphere three metres in diameter with black dots painted all over its inside surface.

The chair remained stationary while the sphere rotated around it. Compared to the position of my head, the sphere rotated as though its axis ran through my ears, so the pattern of dots either rose up in front of me or cascaded downwards depending on which way the sphere was turning.

This equipment is much easier on the body than the PAM because you just have to sit there while the sphere does the turning. Dr. Howard turned the sphere forward for a few minutes then reversed its direction. As the dots moved past my eyes I got a powerful sensation that I was either tilting forwards or backwards, but there was never a complete illusion of tumbling end over end.

Since my body was actually sitting still, my organs of balance were not being stimulated at all. The brain relies mostly on the eyes for information because they provide more detail than any other organ. But it must also consider what's coming from all the other inputs, and it will consider an absence of signals from the other parts of the body as a sign that nothing is happening. Those are two very powerful and conflicting messages, one from those trustworthy eyes that see motion, and an absence of signals from all the other sources because there is in fact no motion of the body at all. Does majority rule?

In a good old Canadian compromise the brain tries to reconcile both messages and creates an artificial reality that the body is in some kind of tilted position, either forwards or back. The amount of tilt depends on the individual, which is the basis of the research. Why are some people more susceptible to the illusion than others? Is it possible to completely ignore it? I found that I could make the illusion go away for a few seconds, but it would quickly return.

Dr. Howard has taken this to another dimension with a rotating room, complete with furniture, curtains on the windows, dishes on the table, everything tacked down securely so the room can rotate completely around like a huge box on a barbecue rotisserie. In this case, sitting in the chair suspended in the middle of the room, the axis of rotation passed through my forehead, so I saw the entire room and its contents spinning around in front of me as though I was looking at the hub of a big wheel. After a few minutes of turning I felt as though I was tilted on my side even though my body was perfectly upright and motionless.

In everyday life all the different motion and balance signals coming into our brain more or less agree, allowing us to walk down the street without giving it much thought. When they don't agree, we not only stagger like a drunken sailor, we throw up like one as well.

I own a sailboat and have watched some of my passengers experience the gruelling affair of seasickness on rough days, and I'm not totally immune to it myself. Many people think the best place to be on a boat when the stomach starts to turn is lying down below in the cabin, which is exactly the wrong place to be. Even a somewhat seasoned sailor can feel queasy after only a few minutes down below on a rough day. Like the astronaut, a person inside a boat doesn't see the rolling motion but their organs of balance feel it. The best place to be is up on deck watching the horizon. The straight line where the Earth meets the sky provides a steady reference for up and down so you can keep your head level while the rest of your body balances against the motion of the boat. An even better remedy is to take the wheel and steer, which forces you to concentrate on where you're going, puts you in control and gives you something else to think about besides your stomach.

Why the confused brain takes it out on the stomach is not completely clear. One leading theory suggests the reason we lose our lunch when we're disoriented is because the brain believes the body has been poisoned. Oddly enough, one of the first symptoms of poisoning is a loss of balance. Since most poisons get into the body by way of the stomach, perhaps the brain is programmed to get rid of the stomach contents as a defence mechanism.

Throwing up is uncomfortable enough, but spewing in space can be fatal. Imagine vomiting while wearing a space suit. In weightlessness the vomit remains floating in front of the face, trapped inside the helmet. The astronaut could choke to death sucking the vomit back in on the next breath. That's why space walks never take place at the beginning of a mission. The astronauts wait a few days until everyone gets their "space legs" before getting into a suit to go outside.

My experiences in the PAM and rotating rooms were just a hint of how astronauts prepare for the loss of up and down that happens in space. In orbit they use the position of their feet to adopt a personal down which becomes a reference for everything else. In fact they become so well adapted to an omni-directional life that they find it very disorienting coming back to Earth. Many astronauts and cosmonauts, especially those who have spent months on the *Mir* space station, have told me the sudden return of all the sensory inputs is quite overwhelming. In space their brains learn to ignore the normal signals from the skin and organs of balance, so when those signals suddenly return back on Earth, their brains need time to relearn how to interpret those signals.

For about a week after landing, astronauts are careful not to turn their heads too quickly because the overactive balance organs turn the world on its side. You can usually tell who's been in space recently because of the way they walk down the hallway and have difficulty turning corners, usually stumbling into the wall on the opposite side. They tend to drop things, especially if they've been in space a very long time, like Russian cosmonauts returning after months in orbit. Having adapted to an environment where objects left in the air tend to stay there, astronauts on the ground let go of things without setting them down on a table, then jump at the sound of a sudden crash to the floor.

If you really want to play a practical joke on an astronaut just back from space, turn out the lights. Without the visual cues that they have become totally dependent on, they have no way of knowing where up and down, or even their limbs, are located. It's apparently a very distressing feeling.

Everyone who travels in space gets a new look, thanks to a physical transformation affectionately known as "puffy face and bird legs." Fluids shift to the upper torso by the heart, which normally has to pump blood up from the legs against gravity. In weightlessness the heart continues to pump towards the chest, giving astronauts rounder faces and squinty eyes. Sometimes the change is so dramatic that crew members have to get used to recognizing the new faces of their crew mates. The effect worked to the advantage of Roberta Bondar. She didn't need to wear glasses during her flight in 1992: weightlessness had restored her eyeballs to their proper round shape.

Some of the changes taking place in the body are more than cosmetic, they are downright harmful. The same shift in body fluids that produces the puffy face also triggers a loss of red blood cells. The extra fluid in the chest area is interpreted by the body as too much blood so red cells are eliminated, giving long-term space travellers an anemic appearance. It also challenges their immune system, because of the loss of important killer T-cells—the sentinels that fight off foreign invaders. Why immune systems are suppressed in space is not clearly understood. It's probably a combination of exposure to radiation from space, the psychological stress of training, blast-off and performing flawlessly, plus the physical stress of blast-off and adaptation to weightlessness. Similar immune suppression is seen in elite athletes. What this means for long missions in the future no one knows; perhaps it will amount to nothing more than a lot of colds on the space station.

A greater concern is the loss of calcium in the bones. Without the daily pounding pressure of standing and walking, the unstressed bones of floating astronauts become thinner and more brittle, like an advanced form of osteoporosis. Left unchecked, people returning from long missions could be permanently crippled by brittle bones too weak to support their weight.

A number of ingenious exercise devices have been developed to counteract these effects. The current methods are exercise bicycles or treadmills with built-in bungee cords that loop around the shoulders so the astronauts can run in space. But those exercise only muscles and bones. A new generation of machines under development at the NASA Ames Research Center in California attempts to deal with the fluid shift as well.

I tried a few of these strange contraptions including a bicycle-powered turntable, which is basically a large round platform with an exercise bicycle on top. The bicycle seat has been replaced with a reclining chair so when I sat down I was lying on my back with my head near the centre of the disc. The bicycle pedals are mounted near the rim of the disc and with a few easy cranks the entire platform spins around. The idea is to force blood towards the feet by the spinning action while the rest of the muscles are exercised by pumping the pedals. It's a nice idea. The only problem is watching the ceiling spin around at a dizzying pace during your exercise routine. I was told to keep my eyes closed to keep my stomach in place but I managed to sneak a peek anyway. Surprisingly it didn't feel as strange as my experience in the PAM. With my head near the centre of the disc it wasn't moving as fast as the rest of my body so the spinning looked faster than it actually felt. The space version of this machine will probably come with a set of blindfolds.

Two other space exercise machines used simpler and, well, comical-looking approaches to getting fluids to the lower body. One makes the user look like a human jack-in-the-box. You stand inside a large accordion-like bellows which reaches up to your waist. Two straps over your shoulders hold it up like a single pant leg from a clown outfit. When you bend your knees the bellows collapses and air rushes out. But valves restrict the air from going back in when you try to straighten up. This provides resistance for your muscles but it also creates a vacuum around your lower body, which draws fluids down from your chest. It works but sure looks funny. All it needs is an accordion and you could play circus tunes while doing deep knee bends.

The final device also used air pressure but it could also change your weight. A large clear plastic skirt was wrapped tightly around my waist, draping all the way to the floor like a full ballroom gown. The bottom of the skirt was large enough to encompass a treadmill that I stood on. An air pump could suck the air out of the skirt and pull me down onto the treadmill so I felt heavier. It was powerful enough to buckle my knees if it was turned right up.

The experience became more interesting when the controller reversed the fan, increased the air pressure and made me lighter. As I ran on the treadmill my steps became larger. With my weight reduced two-thirds I was running on Mars, each step at least twice as long as my Earthly strides. The first Olympic Games on the red planet will smash all records. When the controller reduced my weight to one-sixth the gravity of the Moon, I had to slow down because each step sent me aloft for such a long period I began to fall forward and lose my balance. I gained a new respect for the *Apollo* astronauts who had to deal with reduced gravity while carrying bulky life-support systems on their backs. When you spend so much time floating above the ground in the low gravity it's easier to hop rather than run so you will have both feet under you for support when you land. That explains the bunny-hopping astronauts seen in film clips from the Moon.

Whether it's on another world or floating around this one, living in space is living in a strange new environment that was not meant for humans. But thanks to the brain's amazing ability to adapt to new situations we are going there anyway.

Chris Hadfield continues to play a big part in the space program. He told me he would like to be commander of the space station, and if there were ever a mission to Mars, he would sign up in a heartbeat. He truly is a Right Stuff kind of guy, always wanting to push the frontier of human experience farther outwards.

Growing up with that daring attitude was what I assumed all astronauts needed to get into space, but now there is a new breed of space traveller, no less dedicated, but coming from a different background and in space for a different reason. These are the scientist astronauts who are taken up as passengers so they can continue the study of the human body in space by studying it in space. Canadian astronauts Roberta Bondar, Bob Thirsk and Dave Williams are medical doctors who used themselves as guinea pigs to find out how to live in an environment where the bones lose calcium, the blood loses red cells and the body changes shape almost as though it is evolving into a new form . . . *Homo spaciens?*

Julie Payette calls herself a new generation of career astronaut, just an ordinary hard-working person with a difficult but tremendously exciting job to do. And while NASA has done its best to make flying in space look routine, it's not.

We saw in 1986 how terribly wrong a space shuttle launch can go, all because of a leaky rubber gasket and bad management decisions to fly in cold weather. Those horrifying images of the shuttle *Challenger* exploding in an orange ball of flame still linger over every launch, especially when you know one of the people strapped inside.

Whenever I see a space shuttle sitting on the launch pad, I see a vehicle that is older than most cars on the road. All five shuttles in the fleet were built in the seventies and eighties. The white bird clings to the belly of its enormous orange fuel tank like a woodpecker to a tree. Three massive rocket engines in the tail will gulp 1,400 kilograms of fuel every second when they ignite. Almost two million litres of highly explosive liquid oxygen and liquid hydrogen in the huge belly tank feeds that thirst: a modern-day Hindenburg waiting for a flame. Strapped to the sides of that giant bomb are two white solid rocket motors, the world's largest firecrackers. Packed with a solid mixture of aluminum and ammonium perchlorate, they ignite instantly and provide three-quarters of the power that lifts the shuttle off the ground. Once lit, the solid boosters cannot be stopped until they burn out two minutes later.

On more than one occasion, right at that moment of truth, when the fires in the main engines are first ignited, computers have sensed that full power has not been reached, a task they must achieve in less than six seconds. The entire system is shut down before the unstoppable solid rockets are lit, an instant before anything leaves the ground. During the next seconds of silence the crew, strapped to their seats and perched atop all this explosive firepower, waits anxiously. This is the most vulnerable time for everyone aboard. When the spacecraft is fully loaded with fuel, engines hot, with the escape bridge swung back out of reach in the fully retracted position, a leak of rocket fuel or a faulty valve could trigger a fire at the base of the shuttle and catastrophic explosion with little chance of survival. To make it to safety the crew must wait precious seconds for the access arm to move back into position, unfasten their safety harnesses, scramble through the hatch and tumble into one of five baskets attached to slide wires 360 metres long that reach from the top of the tower down to an underground bunker designed to withstand an explosion of the entire vehicle.

Several launches have been shut down at the last second in this way; so far, no fires have broken out and no crew has made an emergency exit.

If the main computer is happy that the engines have reached their limit, another command is sent to the solid rocket boosters which ignite like roman candles. They are called rocket motors but there are almost no moving parts involved. The two white tubes are packed with solid fuel with star-shaped holes running up the centres along their entire length. Igniters spark a white-hot flame that shoots up the central holes igniting the fuel from the inside out. The outer skin of the rockets bulges out from the explosive pressure within. Rubber seals, the famous O-rings, are squeezed between joints and struggle to contain the internal inferno. Less than a second after the solids ignite, the upward force of all the engines and boosters is greater than the weight of the shuttle. It has reached the point of no return. Explosive bolts holding the roaring vehicle to the pad release a few thousandths of a second later and with nothing more than raw power, more than two million kilograms of machinery defies gravity and rises straight up into the air.

This isn't flight: it's balancing on a flame. The engines steer the white-hot rocket exhaust like a juggler's hand balancing a baton on end. A failure at this point would send the vehicle crashing straight back down in an all-consuming fireball. Liftoff is nothing more than a controlled explosion that blows the whole shuttle and its brave crew off the planet.

The terrific roar, an endless thunder that crackles and rips the air, beats against your chest like a thousand fists. Rising out of its own billowing cloud of smoke, the shuttle grazes frightfully close to the tower that supported it, so close the commander watches it pass by his shuttle window. Then, rising on a pillar of flame it rolls on its back and heads out over the ocean.

I can almost see through the side of the shuttle cabin, see one of Canada's own, strapped into the seat with a big grin on the face, head tossed around inside the helmet by the harsh vibrations of all that horsepower. Fly, bird . . .

Sitting at one of the consoles in launch control is a person every astronaut hopes got a lot of sleep the night before, the range safety officer. This single individual has an ominous responsibility. As soon as the shuttle rises off the pad the officer watches a map of the Kennedy Space Center and the Florida coastline. A red line runs parallel to the coast and another line follows the path of the shuttle heading out over the Atlantic. If something goes wrong and the shuttle begins to veer off course back towards the coastline, the safety officer's finger hovers over a red button. If the shuttle crosses the red line, the button is pushed. Explosives attached to the sides of the solid rocket motors detonate, destroying the entire vehicle . . . and the crew. All of the astronauts who fly on the shuttle know that their lives will be sacrificed for the sake of millions of people living in Florida.

They try not to think about that possibility.

Less than a minute after liftoff the shuttle approaches another critical moment when it breaks the sound barrier while still travelling almost straight up. It's called maximum aerodynamic pressure but everyone in the space business remembers it as the moment *Challenger* was torn to pieces. The engines are powered back to ease through this critical barrier. A small white cloud appears briefly around the nose, the signature of the shock wave formed as the shuttle pierces the speed of sound. Once through the barrier the engines are brought back up to speed with the words "Go at throttle up," the last words spoken by Dick Scobee, commander of the doomed shuttle *Challenger*.

Since that fateful day, shuttles have continued on up, "All systems nominal" but no time to breathe easy just yet. One more critical hurdle on the road to space must be jumped, solid rocket motor separation. Only two minutes into the flight, having boosted the shuttle from zero to more than 5,000 km/h, the two white booster engines have already run out of fuel. The long flames begin to flicker and die, then with a sudden flash of explosive bolts the burnt-out firecrackers are cast off to fall back into the Atlantic.

Everyone on the ground and in the shuttle breathes a sigh of relief. The most dangerous part of the launch is over.

Now, if something goes wrong there are options for escape. The sky outside the windows turns from blue to black as the shuttle, weighing only half what it did at liftoff, accelerates like a true missile up to almost 30,000 km/h, twenty-five times the speed of sound. Astronauts are pressed into their seats, feeling three times heavier than they did on the ground.

I've experienced the force of three g's in a centrifuge. That's the big arm with a cabin on the end that swings around in a circle increasing the apparent weight of the passenger. At three g's your arms feel like logs but they can still be lifted without too much effort. There is no discomfort breathing although it does feel like someone is sitting on your chest.

Astronauts feel all that plus a little more because during this part of the flight the shuttle is flying upside down, so they are also hanging from their shoulder straps.

Finally, after eight and a half minutes of this pounding pressure, the engines are silenced and everyone feels like they have been thrown over a bottomless cliff into a perpetual state of falling. Welcome to space.

I know my chances of taking that ride are pretty slim. There was a time during the eighties when I thought I had a remote chance of flying because NASA announced a journalist-in-space program. But that chance went up in flames with the *Challenger* accident. Immediately following the disaster that took the lives of seven astronauts, including the first civilian, Christa McAuliffe, NASA announced there would be no more civilians on the shuttle. Even if the opportunity did arise, would I have the right stuff to cope with the stresses of launch, disorientation, motion sickness and loss of up and down? We all have our fantasies.

A number of private companies are trying to develop low-cost space planes that will offer tourist flights into space, possibly up to an orbiting hotel, maybe even to a golf course on the Moon. Having tasted just a bit of what it takes to leave the planet, I suspect that many of the first tourists in space will spend a lot of time with their heads in air-sickness bags.

Whether I make it into space or not, I have gained one spinoff benefit from learning about the effects of space travel that applies to life back here on the ground . . . it keeps the back seat of my car clean.

A friend of mine once asked me to drive his youngest son to their cottage for the weekend. As we buckled him into the back seat I was handed a bunch of towels.

"He always gets carsick; use these to clean up the mess," my friend said with a sheepish look. "He hasn't eaten much, so it shouldn't be too bad."

Great. Now he tells me. But then it dawned on me how the problem might be solved. Of course I didn't want puke all over my car, so I said, "Do you have a pillow?"

"That won't work, he doesn't sleep in the car."

"No, I don't want him to sleep. The pillow will keep him from getting sick."

I put the pillow on the seat and had the boy sit on top of it so he was high enough to see out the window. For the first time probably in his life he enjoyed the two-hour ride to the cottage and we didn't need the towels at all. The secret? I made sure he was sitting high enough to look out the windows so he could see that the car was moving instead of just feeling it.

Kids sitting in the back seat of a car often get sick because of the same sensory conflict experienced by astronauts. When the car starts moving, the information coming from a child's eyes does not agree with what that child's body feels.

Strapped low in the seat, they are too short to see the scenery passing by out the windows. His view is restricted to the inside of the car, which, relative to his head, is not moving much. But the rest of his body feels very strong movements from the car itself as it bumps down the road, changes lanes, rises over hills, dips through hollows and leans around corners. The two conflicting messages, one saying the body is moving, the other saying it is not, are confusing to the brain and that confusion is what makes the child lose his lunch.

That also happens to people who try to read in a car. Focusing on a book creates the same visual illusion of not moving. So unless you have an iron stomach, don't read in the car, and if your kids are constantly throwing up in the back seat, make sure they sit high enough to see out the windows and you will probably have a much more enjoyable trip.

Who says there are no benefits from the space program!

We've gone to a lot of trouble getting ourselves off the ground. Now the age of space exploration is giving way to exploitation. People are travelling into space to live and work. Their homes and workplaces are getting so large we will soon see them from the ground. Ever wondered what is going to happen to all those space stations when we are through with them?

SPACE STATIONS AND SPACE JUNK

*You needn't be a rocket scientist to
know what could drop on your head*

STAFF IN THE NEWSROOM OF CBC Halifax must have thought they were being attacked by a terrorist bomber in 1979 when a long-haired young man in a leather jacket and motorcycle helmet burst through the doors yelling, "Have you seen it yet?"

I rushed to the windows, searching the sky. "It's passing over the city right now and could come crashing down!" All work in the room came to a stop. The declaration certainly got everyone's immediate attention.

"Seen what?"

"*Skylab*—it's a huge space station that's falling out of orbit and could come down on this city any minute."

By this time several people had gathered at the window to search the skies as well as check out this stranger with the Chicken Little story.

Finally someone asked, "Who the heck are you anyway?"

Of course I realized that I was a complete stranger to these people and quickly explained that I was a freelance science writer from Toronto who had come to the East Coast to write a series on the oceans. But on the way to the CBC I had heard on the radio that the American space station

Skylab, the largest object in orbit, was crashing down to Earth. The seventy-ton station had been abandoned in space for five years and its orbit had decayed to the point where it was running out of control into the Earth's atmosphere.

Controllers on the ground could not predict exactly where it was going to crash or how much debris would reach the ground. All they knew was its flight path, which happened to carry it right over the city of Halifax. Nothing that large had ever fallen from space so it would produce a spectacular light show in the sky as it burned up. It could also turn into flaming wreckage raining down on the city.

The news director pointed to a door and said, "Get into the studio right now!"

Thus began my first live gig as a freelancer. Fortunately, *Skylab* managed to stay aloft long enough to pass over the city. In fact, it made its way halfway around the world to a remote area of northern Australia where debris was scattered over hundreds of kilometres. No one was killed, although one airport employee was close enough to capture the fireball on film and apparently one piece of debris killed a cow.

You can get an idea of *Skylab*'s size at the Air and Space Museum in Washington, D.C. It was made out of leftover parts from the giant *Apollo* Moon rockets. The four-storey-high version in the museum is a backup training model showing the main living quarters. Not shown is a science lab half as large again that was attached to one end; when the astronauts docked their *Apollo* capsule to the end of that, the whole structure grew to 36 metres, longer than two Greyhound buses. That's a lot of junk to drop from a 400-kilometre altitude.

It's too bad *Skylab* was lost because there was nothing

wrong with it. The interior had the space of a two-bedroom house, a true luxury for astronauts who had travelled to the Moon in capsules with less room than a minivan. *Skylab* afforded the first opportunity for astronauts to actually live in space with enough room to move around without bumping into something or each other. One section of the living quarters was a ring of storage lockers that ran all the way around the interior of the cylinder. Their flat doors formed a track that the astronauts could actually run around even though the whole station and everything in it was weightless. The circular motion of their bodies kept their feet on the track the way a ball stays out on the end of a string when you swing it around your head. Three crews lived in it for months at a time performing hundreds of scientific experiments, but since men had already walked on the Moon, the heyday of large space budgets was over, so the lab was left on its own. There were plans to return to *Skylab* with the new space shuttle, but that project was so far behind schedule it couldn't get off the ground in time to save the station from its death plunge. The fall of *Skylab* was the equivalent of watching a U.S. $2.6-billion high-tech scientific laboratory burn to the ground.

Space junk has been a concern since the beginning of the space program. Every time a rocket is launched, boosters, nose-cone fairings, restraining clamps and dozens of explosive bolts end up orbiting the Earth as pieces of litter. Even the space shuttles, which are supposedly reusable vehicles, shed their giant orange fuel tanks and direct them to a fiery plunge over the Indian Ocean after every launch. More than eight thousand objects are orbiting the Earth at this moment; less than one in ten is a working spacecraft.

Most of these objects eventually fall back to Earth, becoming brilliant fireballs as they plough through the atmosphere at 28,000 km/h. There is a good chance that a falling star you saw one summer night was actually a piece of space junk falling from orbit. Smaller pieces burn to cinders before reaching the ground, but every now and then a larger one makes it to the Earth's surface.

One of the first Russian space stations, called *Salut,* came down in parts of Argentina. No one was hurt. Another Russian craft, a military spy satellite called *Cosmos 954,* came down in the Canadian Arctic spreading its radioactive fuel over the tundra. And as recently as 1997 a robotic probe intended to reach Mars failed to light its third-stage engine and fell in Chile. So far, no one other than the cow in Australia has been hurt by this falling space junk but, as cities become larger and more of the land is covered by people, finding a place to crash-land a spaceship is getting harder every day. As we continue to build even larger structures in space, it doesn't take a rocket scientist to figure out that eventually, some piece of space junk is going to fall on someone's head.

The largest structure assembled in orbit in the twentieth century is *Mir,* a space station twice the size of *Skylab*. It's been flying since 1986 and is nearing the end of its life, while construction has already begun on the *International Space Station* which will be as large as a football field. Recipe for disaster?

When a large building is erected on Earth, the designers usually provide both a construction plan and a destruction plan. In space, the destruction is usually a matter of letting whatever it is fall out of orbit. For smaller objects this is not a bad solution because they turn to smoke before they hit the ground. Besides, the Earth picks up tons of natural debris from space every day. A piece of space junk won't make much of a difference. But large structures are a different story because their extra mass gives them more momentum, which means a greater ability to punch through the atmosphere. Combined with a longer burn time because there is simply more stuff to burn, the big stuff can make it all the way to the surface, and the problem is controllers can only estimate where the junk is going to land.

The best place to bring something down is over an ocean where there is little chance of hitting anyone, and little chance of the public actually seeing this stuff fall from space. But hitting a target, even one as big as the Pacific, is not easy when you are trying to steer a piece of metal that has a shape like a dragonfly. Smooth shapes such as the space shuttle can be steered to precise landings, but space stations tend to be conglomerations of modules that stick out in all directions. They were never intended to fly through the air. When an odd-shaped object enters the atmosphere at 25,000 km/h, it begins to tumble end over end. Pieces break off and melt. The whole shape changes, affecting its behaviour in the air. The shape may become smoother so it slips through the air more easily and stays aloft longer. Or it may develop a more blunt shape and fall short. There is simply no way to predict exactly. The space scientists try to come up with a "footprint," an oval-shaped area on the ground usually covering hundreds of square kilometres where they believe the wreckage is most likely to fall. But during the final moments, the entire footprint can move from the ocean to land and populated areas.

The biggest worry at the moment is the fate of *Mir*, currently on an orbit that carries it over most of the world's major cities. The Russian government has found it impossible to come up with the U.S. $200 million needed to keep the station operating and has virtually shut down the program. Some private investors have put up cash in the hopes of turning it into a hotel for ultrarich tourists who would have to cough up U.S. $20 million for a ticket but no one knows whether that venture will actually succeed, considering the enormous cost of renovating the aging station for public use.

American space scientists would prefer to see *Mir* come down so the Russians can devote their limited resources to completing critical sections to the new *International* station. But something must be done soon because without attention, *Mir* will come down one way or another. The fundamental problem with our space program at the start of the twenty-first century is that all our largest vehicles, those that carry people, don't really fly in space.

Technically, they are still within the Earth's atmosphere. Space stations, space shuttles or military spy satellites all fly in low orbits just a few hundred kilometres above the ground. At that altitude there are still thin traces of air that provide a small but significant amount of drag on the vehicle. For short flights of weeks or even months, the drag doesn't have much effect, but over years it eats away at the vehicle's speed causing it to drop lower and lower out of the sky. One of the jobs of the unmanned *Progress* cargo ships that regularly brought supplies up to *Mir* was to use their rocket thrusters to boost the station back up to compensate for the decay in its orbit. The space shuttle provided the same service during its visits. Without those regular boosts, a spacecraft in low orbit follows that old saying, "what goes up . . ."

I had the opportunity to see just how large and complex space stations can be when I was given a private tour of *Mir* by Canadian astronaut Chris Hadfield, who flew up to the station in 1995. Too bad we weren't in space at the time he showed it to me. We were just outside Moscow in the cosmonaut training centre known as Star City. It was once a bustling town of twenty thousand people, but now only a few thousand work in buildings with bricks crumbling from the walls, where weeds grow through uncut grass and hallways are dark and mostly silent. The only part of the Russian space program still operating in 1995 was *Mir*, by far the most successful space program ever flown.

At the training centre, a full-sized replica of *Mir* sits in a stadium-sized building where cosmonauts and visiting astronauts can become familiar with all the systems before visiting the real thing in orbit.

On the outside *Mir* is impressive. Each module, about the size of a tour bus, is wrapped in a white insulating blanket dotted with assorted antennae and communication dishes. Six modules are linked together in an impressive, robust array. It even feels amazing to the touch. The titanium/aluminum alloy used to build Russian spacecraft is a smoothly polished metal welded together with such precision that the seams are invisible to your fingers. The sheer bulk of the station gives the impression of strength and stability. It's hard to believe something that large can be flying around the world every ninety minutes.

Inside, the impression of size vanishes instantly. So much equipment is crammed into the walls, floor and ceiling that there is rarely a space where you can't touch both sides at the same time. Each module serves a different purpose. The central command has the most interior room and serves as a meeting place for meals and socializing. My head almost reaches the ceiling, although in space that wouldn't matter because the body tends to assume a slightly bent position. A small dining table near the centre of the room is served by four T-shaped stools on either side with foot restraints on the floor in front of them. The seat is just a place to steady your body while eating.

A closet-sized washroom complete with air-driven toilet is nestled into one corner and an exercise treadmill has been built into the floor. The command centre itself, the "bridge" of the ship, is a small alcove packed with hundreds of old-fashioned push buttons illuminated from behind. It reminds me of a Second World War submarine. A joystick controls the position of the station, as well as any of the *Progress* cargo ships that approach for docking. Above and behind the control centre, a round hatch leads to the central node and the other modules.

Climbing over the control console, trying not to step on any buttons then squeezing through the one-metre hatch, is awkward, but in the weightlessness of orbit we would fly through effortlessly like Peter Pan.

I tried to imagine being confined to the interior space of a few motor homes for up to a year at a time. It's an endurance test beyond even the submariners of the two world wars. This is one area where the Russians have far more experience than the Americans. Ever since they lost the race to the Moon, the Russian's space program has focused on space stations and long-duration space flight. While American astronauts take short, one-week flights in the shuttle, Russian cosmonauts remain in orbit for months and several have been in space for more than a year. That makes them the experts on the psychological effects of living in space for long periods. A great deal of time is spent before every Russian mission making sure the crew members are compatible with each other. Once in space, a full-time psychologist continually monitors the emotional health of the crew and is on call to resolve conflicts that may arise. A space station is no place for grudges or vengeance. The environment is so hostile that in an emergency the crew depend on each other for their lives.

One of the most important psychological tools at mission

control in Moscow is a two-way video conference room where the cosmonauts can see and talk to their families. I sat in on one of these sessions, which happen only about once or twice a week. Three families were present—representing each of the crew members—and I was even given a few minutes out of the ten-minute window when *Mir* passed overhead. Unlike the American program, where mission control maintains constant communication with the shuttle, the Russians only talked to the crew of *Mir* a few times a day and only during working hours. That's the difference between a short, intense flight and a mission that's up there for the long haul.

A big clock on the wall counts down the minutes to first contact. Each tick of the second hand seems to crank the tension in the room up a notch. I sense uneasiness on the part of the family members, probably because we are there with television cameras. It's not an environment for private conversations. When the big moment finally arrives, the video link fails. All we have is voice contact. Precious minutes are lost trying to find the technical problem, while the family members try to salvage the remaining time with short, stilted greetings. Then as quickly as they came, the cosmonauts are gone, off on another ninety-minute journey around the world.

After the session I ask Victor Blagov, the flight director, what effect these video links with the families have on the morale of the crew. He says talking to family members is quite good for morale, but what the crew really enjoys are conversations with people from the arts. Ballet dancers, musicians, rock stars, whomever the favourite performer of a crew member happens to be, that performer is invited into the conference room for a little chat. The cosmonauts find it so refreshing to talk about something other than space. Spirits remain high for days afterwards.

If humans ever decide to venture out to the planets or beyond, the psychological stresses will probably be the most difficult to endure. The first human mission to Mars will confine the crew to the interior of their ship for eight months just to get there. Within days of leaving the Earth there will be nothing but the blackness of interplanetary space out the windows. At least the cosmonauts aboard *Mir* who remained in orbit for up to a year had the luxury of looking out the window at the beautiful blue Earth passing below, the favourite pastime of everyone who flies in space. But a Mars crew will see the Earth diminish to a bright point of light in the sky within the first week of the flight. As the distance between the spacecraft and Earth increases, dialogue with families and friends back home will become impossible. Signals to and from the ship will take up to twenty minutes each way to traverse the vast distances, rendering communication down to one-way messages, about as personal as phone machines. Confinement, lack of view, isolation and large periods of idle time will push the psychological limits of human endurance. Perhaps the ultimate barrier to travelling between the stars will not be technological, but a barrier of human endurance. Within the confines of their metal lifeboat they will rely on co-operation regardless of age, sex, religion, nationality . . . sounds like we're trying to create a perfect society in space. Is that what the right stuff is, politically correct?

One outlandish concept for reaching other solar systems would push the limits of human tolerance beyond anything ever experienced. The "Generation Starship" is a giant cylinder about fifteen kilometres long and two kilometres in diametre. The entire structure is set spinning to create artificial gravity along its inside walls. Into this big space drum a colony of about ten thousand people, along with their farm animals, tools and all accoutrements needed to be a self-sufficient society are sealed up and sent off on a two-hundred-year journey to the stars. Along the way, the original settlers die off, but their children take over the operation of the ship, then their children and so on until the great-great-great-grandchildren of the original pioneers make it to the destination.

The fact that so far no one has been able to operate a closed biosphere on Earth aside, the greatest challenge would be overcoming the personal conflicts brought on by confining so many people to one small space for such a long time. How many revolutions, changes of command, even mutinies would take place in a ship like that? I can imagine the beleaguered survivors of such a journey asking, "Who's idea was this anyway? Let's go back and see what the Earth is like!"

If we really want to hop among the stars as easily as taking the family for a Sunday drive, we need a drastically different type of spaceship, one that is fast, comfortable and easy on the body. Something perhaps like the *Enterprise*, the fabled starship that cruises through the galaxy every week on our television screens. Have you noticed that no one needs wear seat belts on that ship? Now there's comfort and safety!

It's such a magic moment when the captain sternly looks into the starry distance and says "Engage," or in the old days: "Take us out of orbit, Mr. Sulu." We see the *Starship Enterprise,* elegantly poised above the curving horizon of an alien planet. Its bow slowly turns towards the stars, the entire ship elongates as though it's being stretched, then zap! it's off in a flash.

Meanwhile, everyone inside the ship continues about their business as though nothing has happened. Officers on the bridge calmly mill around their posts, crew members enjoy drinks in the forward lounge, no one seems to be affected by the fact that they just went from zero to six times the speed of light in less than a second. Why isn't everyone plastered against the back wall?

Ah, the beauty of science fiction: Hop into your spaceship and within a one-hour-long episode you can visit two or three planets.

The fictional warp drive that propels the *Starship Enterprise* with such great speed uses a very different principle than the flaming rockets we use today, a principle that in theory, might work. Rather than giving the ship a kick in the behind with a controlled explosion, warp drive manipulates the force of gravity, so the entire ship and everyone on it is pulled at the same time. The engines somehow warp the gravitational field around the ship forming a gravitational wave, which the ship then rides like a surfer. Since gravity affects all objects with the same force, the pull of the warp engines on the *Enterprise* acts on every atom of the ship equally. Everything and everyone "falls" forward at the same speed so nothing tries to take off faster than anything else. Drinks stay on tables, the floor stays under feet, even stomachs stay where they belong. No one feels anything no matter how hard the acceleration.

Nice idea, warp drive. Too bad we're not even close to inventing it. There is just one tiny obstacle that stands in our way . . . the law of gravity. It's the most common and wide-reaching force we know of, yet no one knows how it works. Hold any object in the air in front of you and let it go. Miraculously, without any push or pull from your hand, it instantly races downwards. During the fall, every atom of the object is pulled at the same time in a smooth, silent acceleration. It's amazing and as mysterious as life itself. We think we are so smart when it comes to figuring out how things work, but when it comes to gravity, no one has a clue. Sure we can measure it, and predict its effect with extreme precision, but when it comes to the exact mechanism, that invisible force that is keeping you on the ground at this moment, no one knows. A tremendous amount of time and effort has gone into trying to understand that pull ever since Isaac Newton contemplated the falling apple. Einstein died not knowing gravity's secret. Stephen Hawking and other cosmologists have contemplated extreme forms of the force, black holes, wormholes, the big bang creation of the universe and their effect on space and time, but still can't explain the nature of the force itself. And scientists operating the largest instruments on the planet, giant particle accelerators that smash apart matter into its smallest constituents dream of a "Grand Theory of Everything," one equation that will explain all the forces that hold matter together. The one force that refuses to fit that theory is gravity.

Since we don't know how it works, we can't manipulate gravity the way we can manipulate magnetic and electric fields: we can't build a gravity engine. Since English physicist Michael Faraday figured out the relationship between electricity and magnetism in 1821, engineers have produced all kinds of electric motors, generators, magnetic levitation trains, computer chips . . . but until someone makes a similar connection with gravity, there will be no spacecraft where people walk around as though they are on Earth, and sadly, no warp drive. In the meantime, space flight will always be an uphill battle against gravity.

Sometimes it looks like we've invented anti-gravity machines, especially when you see people floating around in padded rooms, but those people are actually inside an airplane that has climbed to high altitude then been put into a free-falling dive where everything becomes weightless for about thirty seconds. That's not beating gravity—that's just falling with it and usually making yourself sick at the same time.

Months after the trip to Russia I watched television images of Chris Hadfield floating about inside *Mir*. I recognized the different modules from my experience in Russia, but every time he passed from one module to another I lost track of where he was because the modules were arranged differently in space than in the simulator on the ground. *Mir* is affectionately known as "Dragonfly" to the Russians because that's what it looks like. Huge solar panels reach out like insect wings while the modules all stick out from the central node like a segmented body. But that makes the interior of *Mir* very disorienting, because the arbitrarily designated up and down are in a different direction in every module. Whenever Chris floated through a hatch, he could turn left, right, up or down to enter another module where the ceiling and floor were in another orientation. He told me later that he had to keep finding the command centre and turn his back towards it so he could figure out where everything else was. Imagine visiting a house where the floor and ceiling change positions every time you walk through a door.

The new *International Space Station* has been designed so all the rooms are oriented with the same up and down, even though they don't have to be, just to make life easier for the astronauts.

I was looking forward to seeing the Russian space program because it had been wrapped in secrecy for so long during the Cold War. Oddly enough, the first piece of space hardware I saw was not at the space agency or rocket launch site, but in a park in central Moscow. The Park for Soviet Technical Achievement was built in the early sixties as a showcase for advanced technologies that at the time were well ahead of the rest of the world. The large park with huge gold-leaf gates was built in the style of a world's fair, with gigantic theme pavilions displaying modern jet aircraft, electronics, textiles and, of course, the crown jewel of Soviet achievement, the hardware that beat the United States into space. The "Cosmos" pavilion, a huge arching building constructed like an aircraft hangar housed the *Vostok* capsule flown by Uri Gagarin, the first man in space. Unmanned probes to the Moon and other planets hung in the cavernous building like giant insects, silver antennae sticking out of bulbous bodies. People flocked to the park from all over the country to see the wonders of Soviet science. Those were the glory days when the Soviet Union truly was producing cutting-edge technology. How much of that reached the people is another issue.

Today people still come to the park, not to marvel at technology, but to shop. Most of the buildings have been converted to markets where locals can buy everything from turnips to televisions. We had been told that there were still some space artifacts to be seen there but I was not expecting the sight awaiting us as we drove onto the grounds. I leaned forward in my seat and shouted, "Look at that, a *Vostok* rocket!"

Everyone in the van, not knowing a thing about space, said, "Where?"

Suspended above a fountain in front of the space pavilion was the type of rocket that carried the first man into space in 1961. Standing ten storeys high, it was a towering reminder of just how far ahead the Russians were in the early 1960s. Rockets on American soil were less than half the size at that time. No wonder the Russians were the first in space. I marvelled at the different approach Soviet scientists took to rocket design. Rather than a single slender tube with one or two engines on the end, the *Vostok*, later called *Soyuz,* uses a large array of twenty smaller engines clustered together in groups of four. The base of the missile is surrounded by four boosters that flare at the bottom like the skirt of a Cossak dancer.

But as I approached this marvel of the sixties I noticed peeling paint with rust showing through. And to top off the insult, the fountain that once reflected the image of this great achievement had been drained of water so it could be used as a parking lot . . . for American cars. What a strange irony that the two superpowers, who stopped at nothing to beat each other into space, were now represented by a rusty rocket and four-wheel-drive Jeeps. I was stunned. The recently rich Russian citizens wanted nothing to do with the old ways.

Inside the space pavilion the same scene played out even more dramatically. American cars for sale, most of them used, lined the walls of the cavernous building while the old spacecraft that once hung from the ceiling were piled in a heap behind a barrier at the far end. How times have changed.

We continued our tour of Moscow looking for more remnants of the Russian space program. At the space agency headquarters a press conference was called to announce the agreement between Russia and an American aerospace corporation. The Americans were buying surplus rocket engines that they were scooping up at a considerable discount. Vultures picking at the bones.

One of the surprising sites, the only one that showed any sign of self-sufficiency was the Krunichev rocket factory, a completely inconspicuous complex in the heart of the city that was totally unknown to Westerners before the end of the Cold War. Behind a tall brick wall, not uncommon around Russian factories, the very ordinary-looking buildings housed a complete manufacturing facility for some of the most potent missiles in the Russian arsenal. Hiding the factory in ordinary buildings in the heart of the largest city provided a perfect disguise for prying U.S. spy satellites. Outside, the dour-looking buildings were covered in city grit. But stepping through an innocuous door, we entered a pristine environment where gleaming *Proton* rockets in various stages of assembly lay side by side like cigars in a box. The *Proton* is a heavy-lift booster, much larger than a *Soyuz,* originally designed to carry nuclear warheads. Now *Proton* rockets are the workhorses of the Russian fleet, carrying large commercial satellites into orbit. At least a half dozen of the behemoths lay on their sides in one giant room. Railway tracks ran the length of the room towards large doors at one end where specially designed covered railway cars could swallow the missiles so they could be whisked unnoticed out of the city to their launch site in Kazakstan. Now the *Protons* were for sale to anyone who wanted a cheap ride into space. They can lift as much as any other large booster, and because their design hasn't changed in more than twenty years, it has the best record for reliability of all rockets and the infrastructure for launching them has been in place for even longer. *Protons* are on the open market, offering low-cost access to space . . . a bargain at only U.S. $70 million a flight. American rockets of similar size are more expensive and a space shuttle launch costs about $500 million.

I walked between the gleaming cylinders and noticed strips of paper taped to the side of each one, labels announcing the customers awaiting a ride into space: Westinghouse, Irridium, Norstar, all American companies. Yes, times have changed but the rockets are still flying, which means more hardware will be launched over our heads and more junk will eventually come crashing down. It will be interesting to see what happens when the environmental movement moves to orbit.

CANNON FODDER

Embarrassing moments in applied science

A SCIENTIST ONCE ACCUSED me of having all the fun. It was during a television setup in a lab where a new "breakthrough treatment" for cancer had been announced. I was there in my least favourite role as a reporter scrambling at the last minute to get a story together for the evening news.

As the cameraman struggled with lights and the sound technician boldly reached up under the sweater of the scientist to pin the microphone on his shirt, the expert looked at me and said, "You come rushing in here when a new discovery is announced. Meanwhile we've been working years to get to this point. You catch all the excitement then dash off to the next exciting discovery while we're still here facing more years of work."

He was partly right. I don't always see science in action. A new announcement is only the end product of countless failed experiments, mistakes and lucky accidents. That's how the scientific process works, by trial and error. But occasionally I do catch some science gone wrong, and sometimes those mistakes can be hilariously funny.

I've witnessed two occasions where simple errors led to

harmless but embarrassing results. One was at the Avalanche Control Centre in the Rocky Mountains, the other was at an aircraft manufacturer and both involved cannons.

High in the Selkirk Mountains of British Columbia, a proud detachment of the Canadian Army fires big guns against a deadly enemy . . . avalanches. They call themselves the "Snow Punchers" and every winter they load up their Howitzer 105-mm cannons and shoot down dangerous precipices of snow in one of the largest avalanche control programs in the world. Since 1962 the Snow Punchers, working with a team of scientists and meteorologists, have protected the Trans-Canada Highway and railway which thread their way through a narrow, forty-kilometre-long V-shaped valley, Rogers Pass.

The pass has been an important link to the West since 1885 when the railway first went through. But the steep sides of the valley make it a trap for travellers who have nowhere to run when avalanches roar down the slopes, which happens regularly. Snow sheds were built to cover parts of the railway but they did not afford enough protection. When the highway was officially opened in 1962, the more elaborate avalanche control program was begun and since then, no lives have been lost, a tribute to the efforts of the snow-watching scientists and the snow-punching military men. However, the day I visited the operation, the snow seemed to be winning the battle.

It was early winter and snowing hard the day I arrived, perfect conditions for an avalanche. Rogers Pass is a spectacular valley with steep snow-covered peaks rising almost straight up more than fifteen hundred metres on either side. This notch in the mountain range receives some of the heaviest snowfalls in North America thanks to its position at the junction of two climate zones, one from the mountains and the other from the ocean. Warm humid air from the Pacific is forced up the sides of the mountains then funnelled through the pass. The warm air cools as it rises, dropping moisture in the form of heavy snow, ten metres of it every year. The combination of heavy snowfall and steep-sided valley makes the pass prone to large avalanches not found in other parts of the world.

It wasn't terribly cold when I arrived but the snow didn't stop falling for the two days I was in the pass. Large wet flakes accumulate on the ground so fast that boot prints disappear in a matter of minutes. At daybreak the cars are almost completely buried under the fluffy stuff. By the time I had swept all the snow off the car, the side where I had begun was completely white again. This thick, damp snow is able to cling to steep slopes more easily than colder powder snow, making it more of an avalanche hazard.

The Snow Research and Avalanche Control Centre is a combination weather office, ski shack and communications hub. Parkas, snowshoes, skis and shovels line the entrance hallway while snow cats and four-wheel-drive trucks stand at the ready outside. The centre operates twenty-four hours a day during snow season, gathering data from monitoring stations throughout the pass, deciding when the threat of an avalanche could pose a risk to traffic on the highway. Part of that risk assessment is actually going outside and measuring the condition of the snow.

Armed with shovels, Silvan Hubert and I head out to a test site to have a look at what is happening beneath the surface. I am reminded of my childhood in Orillia, Ontario, when snow piled up to the eaves of the house. The snowbank behind the research centre towers well above our heads. "We have to dig right down to bare ground," he says, attacking the white mountain with his shovel.

"You've got to be kidding, we'll be here all day," I whine.

"Don't worry. This is new snow, it's easy to move." He replies without interrupting his furious digging. He is right. In a matter of minutes we have cleared a deep trench like two kids digging a snow fort. With the loose material cleared away, Silvan examines the walls of the trench with the skill of a surgeon. Using a broad scraper he smoothes the crystals from the wall of snow then inserts thermometers and moisture metres at various levels. Shavings are scraped onto a black velvet cloth to be examined under a magnifying glass.

"Hmmm," he mutters, recording his observations on a chart.

"So what's the prognosis, Doc?" I ask after watching several minutes of this close scrutiny.

"You see this layer?" He points to a slightly darker line about a metre down from the surface.

"That is called depth hoar and it could mean trouble."

Snow comes in many forms. The classic six-sided flakes that drift down from the sky are just the beginning. The crystals change shape as they lie on the ground. Pressure of more snow falling on top will shorten their crystals as will temperature changes throughout the day and overnight. Early in the season, when the ground is still not completely frozen, heat rises from the ground up through the snow carrying moisture with it, like water evaporating off a lake in the summertime. When the temperature drops well below zero at night, the moisture freezes around snow crystals just below the surface of the snow, forming an icy layer.

Silvan hands me the magnifying glass to see the effect. The

hoar snow looks like tiny ball bearings, much more rounded than the pointy crystals in the layer above it.

"This layer is very unstable because the round crystals don't stick together very well. Let's see if it passes the fist and finger test."

He pushes his fist into the top layer of snow making a hole up to his wrist, then slowly pulls his hand out. The snow retains the shape of the hole. He repeats the action using four fingers and the snow still holds. When he tries the same test in the hoar layer, the snow crumbles and falls away.

The final test for stability is the tilt test, where a block of snow including the hoar layer is cut away and set on a platform. The base is slowly tilted to about thirty degrees, the angle where most avalanches begin. The hoar layer can act like a lubricant, allowing the layer on top to slide down the slope as a slab. This is the most dangerous type of avalanche, racing down the mountainsides at speeds over 160 km/h. All they need is a trigger. Silvan taps lightly on the edge of the tilted platform. The top layer of snow slides off and cleanly falls to the ground.

"I think it's time to close the highway."

Before the decision is made to bring out the big guns, Silvan consults with his colleagues who have gathered snow and weather reports from other areas. They compare the information to decades' worth of avalanche data stored in a computer. As the snow continues to fall outside, the call is made to close the barriers on the highway and bring in the army.

The Snow Punchers are proud to be the only regiment in the country who shoot live ammunition at real targets, so they approach the operation with the seriousness of battle. A camouflaged ammunition truck towing a Second World War–vintage cannon rumbles in ready for action. The army considers this service an opportunity to train the troops in artillery firing so everything is done with brisk military muster. The six-man crew leaps out of the truck in army fatigues and quickly manhandles the cannon into firing position. Seventeen specially designed roadside cannon platforms have been built throughout the pass precisely for this purpose. From these positions the big gun can reach 170 predesignated targets, areas where snow piles up quickly along both sides of the valley. Some targets are five kilometres away and 1.5 kilometres above gun position.

The Howitzer can hurl its shells eight kilometres, making it a perfect cannon for the job. The half-metre long shells of the big gun pack enough explosive power to knock thousands of tons of snow off the jagged slopes. The idea is to bring the snow down before it piles up to dangerous levels. Once it slides down the hill the snow settles into a denser and more stable form.

Through a chain of command running from the lieutenant, to the sergeant, down through the corporals and privates, the gun is loaded and ready within minutes. Dave Shansberg, supervising scientist of the day, looks over maps of the valley with the lieutenant to discuss the targets that are to be hit. Each one has pre-calculated gun co-ordinates of direction, range and elevation. While the gunner takes aim, Dave hops into his truck and drives farther down range to watch the target area and verify that an avalanche is triggered. He also determines if a proper amount of snow slides down the slope to render the area safe. If too much remains at the top, he calls for a second shot.

I have never seen a large cannon fired before, so the excitement is building. Finally, with everyone in position, the radio crackles and the lieutenant gets the go-ahead from Dave. A sequence of commands is quickly shouted down the line of military rank . . . "Ready!" shouts the lieutenant. "Ready!"

shouts the sergeant. "Ready!" shouts the gunner. Then the same chain of command shouts again, "Fire!" . . . "Fire!" . . . "Fire!" At which point all of them plug their ears.

The rest of us quickly take the cue as the loudest boom I've ever heard blasts out of the cannon's mouth. The long barrel ricochets back, launching the entire structure half a metre into the air.

Looking along the line of fire I can see, for the briefest of moments, a tiny black dot against the distant white snow. It is the shell itself flying through the air at an unnaturally fast pace. It vanishes so fast I'm not even sure I saw it. The supersonic shell rips through the air with a crackling sound that quickly fades into the distance. The lieutenant leans over to me and says, "In a couple of seconds you will hear the boom when it hits the mountain, then a low rumble, which is the snow sliding down the slope."

The seconds tick away. We have to wait for the shell to cover the four or five kilometres to the mountain, then wait for the sound, travelling about half the speed of the shell, to travel back to our ears.

We wait . . . no boom. I look at the Lieutenant. He looks at the sergeant, who looks at the gunner, who looks at the private handling munitions in the back of the truck. The private shrugs his shoulders. The shrug is passed back up the chain of command.

"Must have been a dud," says the lieutenant, quickly turning to shout a new set of orders.

"Reload!" . . . "Reload!" . . . "Reload!"

A flurry of activity follows as the breech of the gun is opened, the empty shell clangs to the ground in a cloud of smoke and a new one is loaded in.

"Ready!" . . . Ready!" . . . Ready!"

"Fire!" . . . "Fire!" . . . "Fire!"

Plug the ears . . .

Bang, crackle, crackle . . . no boom.

Shrugged shoulders all around.

Once again I turn to the lieutenant for an explanation.

"I can't believe two duds in a row. That's never happened before."

Then, like the bad joke where everything happens in threes, they perform the whole operation again. At least my cameraman is getting lots of shots of the action. But the action where it counts, up on the mountain, is simply not happening. This is getting a little tedious and we are all beginning to get a little cold.

During an uncomfortable moment when the lieutenant had to decide whether to continue shooting off these rounds, which cost the taxpayer about 150 bucks a shot, his radio crackles with a message from Dave: "Hold your fire, I'm coming back."

"Hold your fire!" . . . "Hold your fire!" . . . "Hold your fire!"

At least the army makes sure everyone gets the message.

A few minutes later Dave steps out of his truck and declares, "You're shooting over the top of the mountain, you're not hitting it at all."

I can't control my laughter. After all the boasting about firing live ammo at real targets, I burst out, "You missed the mountain? It's not exactly a moving target, I mean, this is your proverbial barn door here, fellas."

The men shuffle around kicking snow with their boots. The lieutenant and sergeant examine the cannon. Everything seems to be in order. They can't come up with an explanation. We all decide to break for lunch.

I was assured that there were no people on the other side of the mountain where the wayward shells exploded, although I'm sure a few grizzly bears had an uncomfortable morning.

To their credit, the army did punch snow that day. After returning to their base they discovered that the three cannons used for this purpose had all been in for maintenance at the same time. Apparently the gunsights from cannon number one ended up on cannon number two, so the gun wasn't pointing in the direction in which it was aimed. That afternoon they returned with another gun and assaulted the white enemy on the hill with seventy rounds, all exactly on target.

Since the avalanche control program has been in place, the highway in Rogers Pass has not been closed for more than three hours at a time and no travellers have been injured by snowslides.

That's a far better record than resort areas where dozens of skiers and snowmobilers are killed every year. During the '97/'98 season, twenty-six people lost their lives in the United States, twenty in Canada. That's well above the long-term average of fourteen and six. Many ski areas do have avalanche control programs using air cannons and explosive darts, but most accidents happen off established trails. More people are taking up winter sports, including backcountry and "extreme" skiers who search for pristine snow in out-of-the-way areas. Some are careless and don't recognize the avalanche hazard. Snowmobile drivers who venture into slide areas are at greater risk because the heavy machines put more pressure on the snow while the riders, wearing helmets and sitting behind noisy engines, cannot hear the snow "talk." Experienced skiers listen for telltale crackling sounds coming from the snow just before it breaks free.

Scientists also fear the threat of avalanches could become worse as the changing climate brings more wet snow to the mountains.

My second cannon misadventure involved a simple oversight that turned an expensive experiment into a worthless failure. Scientists hate to say "oops." Mistakes as simple as a forgotten computer command can wipe out hours of work, or in the case of one aircraft manufacturer, a misloaded cannon cost the company thousands of dollars in damaged equipment.

Bird strikes are serious hazards to aircraft of all sizes, especially during takeoff. Birds on runways underestimate the high speed of an approaching aircraft and fly away too late, often flying right up into an engine or wing.

At 250 km/h, a collision with a bird can do serious damage to the thin aluminum skin of a plane, or worse—cause an engine to fail just at the moment when it's needed most.

In 1988, for example, I visited an aircraft hangar in Toronto where Max Ward, president of Wardair, showed me what was left of an engine from a 747 that had been torn apart by a seagull. Pieces of metal were strewn across the floor as though someone had gone crazy with a hatchet and blowtorch. Normally a big engine like that is not bothered by a bird strike. The gull would become instant salsa then baked and blown out the exhaust in less than a second. But in this case the bird set off a chain of events that almost completely destroyed the engine.

The jumbo jet was leaving Vancouver with a full load of passengers destined for Hawaii. Right at the most critical moment of the takeoff, when the nose wheel lifts off the ground and the plane approaches the end of the runway, the flight engineer detected strong vibrations coming from one engine. A gull had been sucked into the intake and the engine was losing power. He shut it down immediately. Fortunately a jumbo jet is capable of taking off on three engines and thanks to the quick action of the crew the passengers were calmly informed that they would be landing in Victoria for an unscheduled maintenance stop. No one was aware anything unusual had happened.

Back safely on the ground, mechanics were astounded by the amount of damage. The impact with the bird had broken the tip off one of the big titanium fan blades in the mouth of the engine. The broken piece had thrashed around among the other rapidly spinning blades, breaking off more pieces which ripped right through the central core. The big engine had been knocked out of commission in a matter of seconds. It wasn't a pretty sight for the bird either. The repair bill for the engine came to $3 million. They figured the seagull weighed about three pounds . . . $1 million a pound. Max wasn't too happy about that.

Airports use a wide assortment of tricks to scare birds away from runways. Explosives, sirens, flashing lights, even loud-speakers broadcasting the screams of an injured bird have only limited success. The birds usually figure out the hoaxes and ignore them after a day or so. A few airports employ fal-coners who fly their birds of prey on airport property to scare the seagulls away. It works, but only during the few minutes when the falcon is flying. Birds and airplanes will always share the same air space so manufacturers must design planes to take a strike and keep on flying. That means they have to somehow simulate in the laboratory the effect of a bird flying into an airplane at more than 250 km/h.

This is where my second cannon story comes in. I was visiting the hangars of de Havilland Aircraft, which built propeller-driven commuter planes such as the Dash 8. While wandering through the factory's research area I noticed a large piece of a wing that looked as though someone had gone at it with a chainsaw. I asked my guide, who was a scientist, what had happened and he told me the sad story: an experiment to find out what happens when a plane hits a bird had gone terribly wrong. The unhappy fact is that the best way to accurately simulate a bird hitting a wing at high speed is to fire chickens from an air cannon. A chicken is about the average size of bird that a plane might encounter in flight.

"You fire live chickens through a cannon?" I asked.

"No, they're dead chickens that we buy at the market."

I looked at the damaged wing again. A large dent in the leading edge extended about a metre in both directions. The whole wing was bent out of shape. Interior ribs could be seen through holes where the aluminum skin had been torn away from the rivets.

"A chicken did all that?" I inquired.

"Well not quite." My guide replied sheepishly.

The company had hired a young student for the summer. They gave him some cash and sent him to pick up a few fresh chickens at a local market then load one of them into the air cannon. Apparently someone didn't completely explain the purpose of the experiment to the student. Either that or he didn't cook much.

The scientists gathered around the loaded cannon later that day, turned on a multitude of instruments that would record the event in microsecond detail, checked the sensors mounted all over the wing, then gave the order to fire. It must have been quite a shock when their very expensive airplane wing almost exploded from the impact. Never had they seen such destruction from a single bird. How was it possible for one chicken to inflict so much damage? Was their wing that inferior that they would have to return to the drawing boards and spend millions redesigning a stronger one? There had to be an explanation.

Of course, whenever a mistake is made, everyone turns to the person below them which led, naturally, to the new summer student. "Just what kind of chicken did you put in the cannon?" asked the chief scientist.

"Actually, they were out of fresh chickens, so I bought a frozen Butterball turkey. They were on sale."

"Oops."

So the next time you fly, don't worry about a bird knocking the plane out of the air. But if there's a Butterball turkey heading your way . . .

Part Two
Waterlude

ONE SMALL DROP

The Great Lakes in perspective

A DROP OF WATER GROWS heavy in the sky. Slipping through air currents that can no longer hold it aloft, the globule flattens itself into the shape of a little hamburger bun and cascades from the belly of a cloud. Minutes later it punches a hole in a lake; the walls of the crater it makes on impact shoot upwards into a perfect liquid circle and then collapse back on themselves launching the drop upwards again for a brief glimpse of the sky before it blends with the huge liquid crystal called Georgian Bay. If it avoids the energy of the Sun that tries to draw it back up into the clouds, if it evades the thousands of intake pipes that would siphon it off to factories and faucets, the drop will follow the guiding hand of gravity, spending the next twenty years on a three-thousand-kilometre journey to the sea.

My sailing vessel *Freedom II* swings on her anchor like a large fish hooked on a line beside the spot where the drop has fallen. The storm that produced the drop and its trillion relatives will soon pass so I can continue my own journey down the same watercourse from the heart of the Great Lakes all the way to the Atlantic Ocean. Over the next three years I will see, smell and taste what humans have done to the world's largest store of fresh water. I will witness the colour change as I travel from the crystal blue of Georgian Bay to the muddy brown of the St. Clair River, smell the polluted air that settles over the vast expanse of water and taste industrial waste whenever I dive overboard for a swim. For most of my journey to the sea I will be accompanied by my partner Sandy Bourque as well as creatures big and small who click, whistle and sing beneath the waves.

Long-distance sailing has become a part of my life. I've been able to explore the eastern part of our country in a way that harkens back to the first explorers who arrived here on the power of the wind half a millennium ago. For the last decade I've travelled from the Great Lakes all the way down to the St. Lawrence and out to Nova Scotia. Then, struggling against the prevailing winds and tides, slipped down the eastern seaboard to Cape Cod, New York City, Chesapeake Bay as well as the Florida Keys and Bahamas. When the wind is your fuel and the water your highway, you become tuned to the environment, the wildlife and our impact on it.

Travelling by water makes you appreciate how much liquid covers the surface of our planet and how little of it is fresh and clean. Having seen just a small part of what is essentially a global ocean, I have come to appreciate the Great Lakes as true gems sparkling on the face of the Earth. Nestled in a basin gouged out by the glaciers, they are the largest melt-water pools on the planet left behind ten thousand years ago when the ice sheets retreated. Nowhere else in the world can the hull of my boat plough through thousands of nautical miles touching only fresh water. The Bedouin people living on the Sahara Desert, who sometimes travel many kilometres for a single pail of water, would be astounded at the sight of the

Great Lakes where fresh water reaches all the way to the horizon. They would be even more astounded by the consumption of the average Canadian who uses about three hundred litres a day spraying lawns, washing clothes, and cars and flushing toilets, then runs off to the store to buy bottled water imported from France that costs more per litre than gasoline, when the largest supply of fresh water lies within a stone's throw of this consumer's front door. I would have a hard time explaining that to the Bedouin who use less than ten litres a day each to survive, and a harder time explaining how along most of the Great Lakes shorelines they would not be able to dip their pails into this precious liquid and drink it without getting sick. I guess the only explanation would be that we are spoiled by the abundance of the resource that humans need more than any other: fresh water.

From the shoreline, or from the deck of a boat, the Great Lakes truly are great, covering a quarter of a million square kilometres, an area almost twice the size of England. But while it seems like a lot of fresh water to have in one place, on a global scale it's literally a drop in the bucket. Three-quarters of our planet is covered in water, but most of it, 97 percent, is salty, and most of the fresh water left over is either frozen or unreachable underground. That leaves very little fresh water to fill our lakes and rivers. Take a globe of the Earth in your hands and you will see lots of blue ocean but less than a dozen large lakes. The Great Lakes taken together are by far the largest freshwater system on the face of the Earth. Africa has Lake Victoria, Tanganyika and Chad but none of them is larger than Lake Superior. Lake Baikal in Russia is so deep it contains the most water of any single lake in the world while Lake Eyre in Australia dries up every year. There are no large lakes at all in South America and in North America all the big scattered lakes are in Canada: Athabaska, Great Slave, Great

Bear and Winnipeg. When you compare the size of these lakes to the land area of the Earth they truly are little drops splattered around the globe.

Astronauts and cosmonauts are always astounded at how little time they spend flying over land. Earth is the only planet in the entire solar system with liquid water on the surface, but when you think about the amount of fresh water available for humans to drink, there really isn't very much. Most of the fresh water is locked up in the ice caps at the North and South Poles. Since the 1940s the idea of chipping icebergs off the polar caps and towing them to dry areas has been kicked around but no one has figured out a practical way to do it. That means most of the fresh water in the world is inaccessible.

The majority of what is left, the unfrozen, unsalty water, is hidden underground. We are doing a pretty good job of pumping that dry, but there is still a lot of underground water we can't get to. Even the water on the surface is partly out of reach, taken up by plants, soil and clouds. By the time you eliminate all the water in the world that is not salty, frozen, underground, in plants or in the air, you end up with less than 0.1 percent of the total that is lying fresh in lakes and rivers. To put it another way, if all the world's water were looked at on the scale of a single drinking glass, the amount we could actually sip would be less than one drop. It is upon that drop that human life depends and almost a quarter of the drop sits in the Great Lakes basin. Gems indeed.

Despite their size, the Great Lakes are particularly vulnerable to pollution because they are like a large sink with a very small drain. It takes a long time for the water to flow out. There are really only two exits from the entire system, one down the narrow valley of the St. Lawrence River, the other through evaporation by the Sun. Getting through the lakes to the river takes years, and when water evaporates it leaves the pollutants behind, which concentrates them further. Most pollution that enters the lakes stays there for a long time and from the deck of a boat you can see it first-hand.

Perhaps I'm being a little harsh because there has been a tremendous amount of work cleaning up the Great Lakes since the bad old days of the forties, fifties and sixties. There have actually been agreements between Canada and the United States to take care of the liquid borderline since 1909. The first didn't have anything to do with pollution; it dealt with regulating water flow so power generators and industry could be assured of a steady supply. Then during the forties, agricultural productivity increased dramatically thanks to "Miracle" fertilizers that encouraged plants to grow faster and bigger while DDT and herbicides protected them from insects and weeds. The plants prospered so well that the period has been called the green revolution, when North America turned into the breadbasket for the world. But while the plants on land loved the chemical encouragement, so did the plants in the water. Algae, which are just tiny, one-celled aquatic plants, ate up the fertilizers that washed off the land into the water, then they grew in tremendous numbers, giving the lower Great Lakes a muddy green colour and lining their shores with thick green goo. Unfortunately, when algae die they decompose on the bottom of the lake in a process called eutrophication, which takes oxygen out of the water. Fish living in the lakes suffocated so the green goo on the shorelines became mixed with silver bodies of dead fish. In 1972 Lake Erie, the shallowest of the five, was declared officially "dead." In fact it wasn't dead at all—it was too much alive with algae.

That same year Canada and the United States agreed on the first of several Great Lakes water quality agreements which are supposed to ultimately lead to not only the elimination of phosphates, the main culprit in algae growth, but also much tighter regulations for industries dumping waste. The green goo and dead fish disappeared from the shorelines but then two more problems appeared. The sea lamprey, a parasitic eel with a large suction-cup mouth and a taste for lake trout, began killing all the fish. It was a new predator competing for the same fish that humans like. Scientists were faced with a dilemma: either do nothing and allow the trout to be wiped out by lamprey, or take a chance pouring more chemicals into streams to kill the lamprey larvae without knowing exactly how the chemicals would affect other life. They chose chemicals, and fortunately the lesser of the two evils worked. But in 1977 a review of the water quality agreement showed that a new, more lethal ingredient was being added to the soup mix of pollution . . . toxic chemicals. Mercury and PCBs were showing up in fish as far inland as Lake Superior. This time the culprit was not the dumping of waste directly into the water—the chemicals were raining down from the sky. Because they cover such a large area, the Great Lakes are catch basins for chemicals pouring out of smoke-stacks and tailpipes. That led to another agreement in 1978 that included air quality as part of the Great Lakes management, then yet another in 1987 to deal with the lakes from a more holistic ecological point of view.

Today the lakes are cleaner, but appearances can be deceiving. Toxic chemicals don't show up as easily as green slime. When you get on the water and just follow it from wilderness to the industrial heartland of the country, you can see how much further we still have to go.

My journey began in Georgian Bay, sometimes called the sixth Great Lake. It's a large enough branch off Lake Huron to have its own title. Very little industry and development line the shores leaving the water remarkably clear. Along its eastern shore lie the Thirty Thousand Islands, a bit of a misnomer because in truth there are more like fifty thousand scattered like seeds across the water. Smooth pink granite rocks supporting knarled pine trees silhouetted against a multicoloured sunset sky inspired painter Tom Thomson. It's a uniquely Canadian landscape and a stiff challenge to sailors attempting to navigate among the shallow rocky channels, especially when a six-and-a-half-foot keel is hanging off the bottom of the boat. (On more than one occasion we would use the keel to discover just how hard granite really is.)

It's easy to find wilderness in this environment, to transport yourself back to the way it was before sailing vessels arrived. It's also not hard to see the impact of human activity. My anchorage is among a small group of rocky islands called the Bustards. A small isolated lagoon nestled between the close shorelines is a perfect haven from storms and a perfect hideaway from civilization. I have the lagoon to myself, surrounded by the last tip-taps of raindrops on the water and a pair of loons calling across the mist.

Suddenly a low rumble fills the air and the sharp white nose of a huge powerboat emerges from behind a hill at the entrance to the lagoon. It fills the channel completely, twin diesels growling like angry bears, the thump, thump, thump of music blaring from speakers on deck providing a pulse that bounces off the trees, echoing throughout the enclosure. Then a second white prow appears, identical to the first; there must have been a sale on fifty-foot mega-yachts. The two white giants circle around me, prowling for space. After much manoeuvring and revving of engines, they raft together and settle close to shore. The booming rumble finally ends and I wait for peace to return, but another mechanical sound continues to drone on. The floating palaces are running generators to power the microwave ovens, televisions and dishwashers so necessary for wilderness travel. A few minutes later, two motorized personal watercraft are lowered into the water and begin buzzing around the lagoon like giant annoying mosquitoes. Feeling totally invaded, I haul anchor and leave. We have become so good at surrounding ourselves with artificial environments that we can't see our impact on the real one.

As *Freedom II* heads south, the first big change in the water happens in Lake Huron where the colour turns from blue to green. The temperature is warmer for swimming, but there is a lot of particulate matter . . . stuff suspended in the water from the surface all the way to the bottom. Perhaps it is algae, maybe material kicked up by surf pounding along the sandy shore but it looks strange to me. Lake Huron empties into the St. Clair River at Sarnia, a passage I make on one of the hottest days of the summer. A strong current sweeps the boat under the Bluewater Bridge, which forms a proscenium arch like the stage of a theatre where the curtain rises on a scene of industrial madness. Chimneys line both sides of the river like huge limbless trees. Their tall forms fade into a brown pallor that hangs over the horizon, a photochemical smog from the searing forty-degree temperature. The air has a metallic flavour.

The river instantly changes colour from emerald to creamy green, just like green tea when you add milk. Here and there streaks of brown swirl in the currents. They call the stretch of river south of Sarnia "Chemical Row," a line of refineries and chemical plants that tower over the river banks. I can't help wondering how many hidden drainpipes I am passing over, how many chemicals are churned up in my wake.

Lake St. Clair is a surprise. Not only is it the smallest of the great lakes, it is barely a lake at all. Reeds stick above the surface well offshore. A channel has been dredged all the way across to ensure deep water for the big ships. That lake will probably be a large marsh in a hundred years.

The river winds past the casinos of Windsor and towers of Detroit, then the hulking steel mills that supply the voracious appetite of the American auto industry. While the factories have cut back on their dumping into the water, the river itself continues to be a strong source of pollution for the lower lakes. Decades' worth of chemicals embedded deep in the mud of the river bottom continue to ooze out of the sediments and flow downstream on a daily basis. I'm amazed to see kids swinging off ropes into the muddy water.

The mouth of the Detroit River spills out through a delta reaching almost halfway across Lake Erie, the grey-green lake. Gone are the rotting masses of green slime along the shore. New cottages under construction are a sign that this once-dead lake is now the place to be. A bad reputation can be a bonus for bargain-hunting real estate buyers. There is even a commercial fishing industry struggling to survive although the thought of eating fish from Lake Erie . . . ah, maybe I'm just too old.

While we're anchored in a lagoon off Pelee Island a perfect V-formation of Canada geese swoops down from the sky performing a magnificent synchronized water landing. It's a positive sign that the lake is recovering. They chatter among themselves for an hour, probably discussing the day's flight while munching on plants among the reeds, then settle into a quiet night's rest while still floating. At daybreak, during the stillness of the morning, we are awakened by fifty pairs of flapping of wings beating against the surface of the water as the V-formation rises into the air like a living airliner delivering its avian cargo to warmer climes.

A day-long passage through the giant locks of the Welland Canal ends with the gleaming towers of Toronto standing clearly on the horizon, easily visible from the opposite shore of Lake Ontario. During the six-hour crossing of the lake, more buildings grow out of the horizon like gravestones rising under a line of smog. Five nautical miles offshore a distinct line appears in the water, a boundary between the dark blue of the lake and the light green of Toronto Harbour. Along the line, seagulls forage among bits of floating debris and dead fish. Approaching the city is like slowly turning up the volume on a bad radio station. The roar of traffic accompanied by a cacophony of music provides the background for the sudden appearance of hundreds of other boats all juggling for position as though theirs was the only piece of water to sail on. I feel as though I have brought a Georgian Bay cottage into the heart of the city.

Toronto's inner harbour alternates between olive green and brown depending on the weather. When thunderstorms pass over the city, rivers rise, and the water turns a turgid brown. Many communities along the lakes combine their sanitary system and storm drainage pipes into one sewer system. But during storms, the extra flow of rainwater charging through sewer pipes is more than the sewage treatment plants can handle, so the flow is diverted directly downstream. That's when signs go up on Toronto beaches warning against the hazards of swimming in water infected with fecal coliform, harmful bacteria in human waste. Toronto is blessed with beautiful long sandy beaches that line the Toronto Islands and eastern communities. On hot summer days, thousands of bathing Sun worshippers stroll the sand, but not one of them goes into the water. Performers at Aquarama, the traditional water show at the Canadian National Exhibition, must take disinfecting showers after every performance. In spite of water agreements, the lakes are not clean.

In the late 1980s a photography student performed a dramatic demonstration of how many chemicals are dissolved in lake water—by developing photographs using nothing but water taken directly from Toronto Harbour. The development times were longer, but all the chemicals needed to develop the prints were there. His public show, all pictures of the harbour itself, was one of the most elegant wakeup calls for politicians and environmentalists.

The difficulty with chemical pollution is the durability of the chemicals themselves. PCBs and their kin are very stable and not broken down by shellfish, fish or birds, so they remain in the food chain for a very long time. A more scary effect, if poisoning isn't scary enough, is how many of these toxins behave like sex hormones, affecting the development of animals. Birds with crossed bills, frogs with extra legs and animals with both male and female characteristics have shown just how insidious chemical pollution really is, especially when you consider that we have the same hormones running through our bodies.

East of Toronto the quality of Lake Ontario water actually seems to improve. Towards Kingston and the Thousand Islands the bottom becomes visible in many areas, although much of that clarity is thanks to the filtering action of the lake's newest resident, zebra mussels. Transported from Europe in the ballast water of ships, they were discharged into the waters off the coast of North America and have been working their way inland ever since. The tiny creatures look like striped clams smaller than the nail on your little finger.

Without enemies in our waters they've spread like rabbits in Australia, clogging intake pipes, fouling the bottoms of boats, generally interfering with anything that uses water.

Having worked their way up the St. Lawrence River and the Erie Canal, which connects Lake Ontario to the Hudson River, they are now happily spreading into the Great Lakes. Ironically, waters that are infested with zebra mussels actually become cleaner and bluer. The animals act as filters, eating the algae that normally turn the water green. In one way, the invading mussels are compensating for the extra algae caused by pollution from agricultural fertilizers. Nature is ever resourceful at finding ways to achieve a new balance when a system changes. It is we humans who strive for consistency. The transparent blue water looks nice, but again, as nature adjusts itself, the clarity of the water allows sunlight to penetrate deeper into the water, encouraging weeds to grow more quickly up from the bottom.

Many harbours along the east end of Lake Ontario are clogged with hectares of matted weeds which have reached all the way to the surface forming engine-clogging, propeller-fouling carpets. Hauling up the anchor in these areas is great exercise for the upper body because the anchor dredges up a huge and heavy bouquet of wet weeds. Leaving the expansive horizons of the lakes, the water begins its final run to the sea through the tremendous drainpipe of the St. Lawrence. You can feel the surge of billions of litres of water squeezing through the maze of the Thousand Islands, not a raging torrent, just a steady massive movement of water. It is truly one of the great rivers of the world, the ruling force in the landscape. Where once it roared it is now calmed and controlled by one of the largest engineering feats on the planet, the dams and locks of the St. Lawrence Seaway. Nowhere else can ocean-going ships travel more than two thousand kilometres inland into the heart of a continent. When I reach the locks my boat seems like a toy in a bathtub bobbing alone in the cavernous structures that were built to accommodate eight-hundred-foot-long ships. Six of the watery stairways connected by long canals step down to the sprawling metropolis of Montreal where the river is finally freed to make its final dash to the sea. Passing more industrial stacks, more signs of human exploitation, the river seems to relax; in fact it comes to a complete standstill then backs up.

I have been fortunate to have both the wind and the current at my back all the way downstream from Kingston to Quebec City. The five-hundred-kilometre trip only takes six leisurely days (with no night travel), a pretty good clip for a sailboat. I become used to watching landmarks pass by quickly until I reach the tiny village of St. Tite des Caps, about fifty kilometres beyond the historic cliffs of Quebec City. A typical silver-roofed church with a tall spire dominates the small cluster of buildings and stands like a sentinel on the shore, a ready reference for river navigators. After checking my position on the chart and the water ahead for traffic, I let the autopilot steer the boat while I go below to make lunch.

During the ten minutes or so it takes to boil water for soup, scrounge around for bread and sandwich fixings and make coffee, the church steeple remains visible out a side window. I climb back up on deck and realize we are not making any headway at all. I check the depth sounder to see if we have run aground but it shows plenty of water under the keel. Then I spot the reason for our holdup. On the opposite side of the boat ripples dance on the surface of the water in a confused pattern, forming long curving lines stretching hundreds of metres into the distance. Suddenly the bow of the boat swings to the right. The autopilot spins the wheel in an attempt to correct but it's no use, the boat turns almost completely sideways. Rippling water moves in all directions as though being stirred by a giant spoon, yet there is no apparent reason for it, no submerged rocks or storm in sight.

After several minutes of confusion, wondering if my keel had snagged a fishing net or whether people on shore are secretly watching through binoculars, waiting to see my vessel disappear because I have wandered into a mysterious ship-swallowing vortex, their version of the Bermuda Triangle, it slowly dawns on me that the river has changed identities. At this point it is no longer flowing to the sea, it has met the sea. I am struggling against the incoming tide. Beyond Quebec City the St. Lawrence is an estuary, a sunken valley where the water flows in both directions according to the rise and fall of the tides. Wise travellers make sure they depart on a favourable tide, otherwise hours are wasted fighting tidal flows that can run backwards as fast as the flow of the river itself.

Eventually the shorelines of the St. Lawrence River part company over opposite horizons. There is no real sense of a river mouth, just an opening of the land to the sea. The cliffs of the north shore run up to Labrador while the cliffs of the south shore become the Gaspé Peninsula, two pieces of a continent that were once the boundaries of an inland sea. The geological forces that push continents around the face of the Earth squeezed the Maritime provinces up against the solid granite of the Canadian Shield. Most of the inland sea was reduced to a river valley but at the mouth, near Rimouski or Baie Comeau, the gap has not completely closed and you can still see the remnants of what was once North America's version of the Mediterranean.

The open ocean is a different kind of sailing experience. The water turns from green to the deepest, purest blue you can imagine. Waves grow into long undulations that roll under the hull with a slow rhythm lasting several seconds per beat. The entire boat rides uphill, climbing mounds of water, glides smoothly over the crest and surfs down into liquid valleys on the far side. Even in calm weather the rolling of the sea is ever present. Walking on deck or poking around in the cabin is an exercise in balance control. You quickly learn the sailor's rule: "One hand for you, one hand for the boat."

The vastness of the sea, its tremendous power and stark beauty provide a humbling experience for humans. Even with our sailing technology we are insignificant specks bobbing about, always on the brink of being knocked down or even destroyed by powers far beyond the human scale. This is what most of planet Earth looks like, endless liquid under an endless sky. Winds are steady and strong, driven by currents from the ocean of air above. When one medium becomes restless the other responds with an irresistible fury. The thin grey line off in the distance, the bit of dry ground where humans scurry about is nothing but a fringe to the mighty sea, a low-lying plateau that could be washed over at the ocean's discretion. Caught between these two constantly moving fluids, one made of air, the other made of water, a sailor becomes acutely aware that we don't conquer the sea, the sea lets us pass over it.

Offshore our attention turns to birds. Seagulls and gannets come in extra-large jumbo size, with wings reaching two metres across. The graceful black and white birds sweep across the waves, occasionally dropping from great heights like dive bombers, plunging with a splash through the surface, their beaks becoming spears to unsuspecting prey. As city folk we got a quick lesson in the difference between true seagulls and the "gulls" that hang around the Great Lakes. Most flocks of birds have a few curious wanderers that fly over to check out our solitary boat passing by. On the Great Lakes we often toss bread overboard and are entertained by the ensuing screaming match. As the big seabirds circle around the mast, Sandy grabs a loaf of bread and throws an entire handful of slices into the air. The birds look down . . . curious, then fly away. True seabirds eat fish, not garbage!

We felt like complete idiots sitting there with pieces of bread surrounding the boat. Hopefully some fish found them tasty.

It was during our exploration of the Gulf of St. Lawrence and east coast of Nova Scotia that a new problem of water quality emerged, except this time the water was inside the boat, not under it. Our holding tank was full and there was no place to get it pumped out. All boats that sail on the Great Lakes are required to carry a holding tank for the waste water flushed down the head. (That's marine talk for toilet.) Most marinas have pumps on shore designed to empty the tanks and dispose of the waste properly. This practice is not carried out in most ocean communities because the tides flush the harbours naturally twice a day. That means toilets on maritime boats flush directly overboard. Entire towns forgo sewage treatment for the same reason and even the City of Halifax was dumping raw waste as recently as the early nineties. Since my boat is not equipped with an overboard discharge, this became a rather "heady" issue as the tank reached the limit of its capacity. Eventually the situation began to announce its presence in the summer heat by a certain *je ne sais quoi* aroma.

We were almost to the point of heading back up the St. Lawrence when we finally found a pumpout in Baddeck, a town on Bras d'Or Lake in the heart of Cape Breton Island. Needless to say it provided tremendous relief, but we had to be very careful with our waste water from that point on because the next pumpout wouldn't appear until Saint John, New Brunswick. I had run into this problem before on another trip to Chesapeake Bay along the East Coast of the United States. Asking for a pumpout was like speaking a different language. When you think about the number of boats that head out every day along our coastlines, that's a lot of crap going into the water. If boats were the only source of human waste there probably wouldn't be a problem; after all whales poop in the water too. But the attitude represented by the boats, that the ocean is a naturally flushing toilet, is becoming a serious global issue.

We may not like our waste material but many algae do. They just eat up our sewage, animal manure and chemical fertilizers running off farms as well as millions of tons of other organic effluent we dump into the oceans every day. The free food can cause an overpopulation of the algae known as an algal bloom. The most disturbing part of the process is the appearance of certain species of algae that give back their own waste, toxic chemicals that are poisonous to fish and humans.

"Red tides" have been known for centuries. Lobster and mussel fishermen must shut down their operations every season when the red algae appear in the water. The surprising part of this process is how the poisonous chemicals don't seem to bother the shellfish, something scientists would like to figure out, but they do have a harmful effect on humans who eat the shellfish. Prince Edward Island got a lesson in 1987 with the tainted-mussel scare. Three people died and more than one hundred were sickened from eating mussels that contained toxins produced by harmful algae. Shellfish depend on algae for food but somehow they are not affected by the poison themselves. Researchers are hoping to figure out how they protect themselves so those same protections could be offered to people.

Harmful algal blooms used to be confined to a few areas around the continent but now every state and province along the coast is affected by some form of toxic algae that are affecting fish, plants and people. Something is changing in the oceans and the effects are not trivial. In humans, some of these toxins affect the brain, causing amnesia or temporary memory loss.

Visitors to Florida have seen the water turn brown, stinging their eyes and burning their noses from a kind of algae that also kills fish and even manatees, the beloved "cows of the sea" that live in Florida rivers.

Usually, harmful algal blooms disappear on their own but within the last decade outbreaks have become more frequent, covering larger areas and affecting more people all over the globe. The blooms are like diseases of the oceans where sudden outbreaks cause massive damage for a few weeks then disappear as quickly as they came. Our knowledge of underwater diseases is so limited that scientists don't know if this is an emerging problem or something that's always been there. More people are living along the coast and more people are eating seafood. A good part of the problem is the growing size of our own population. The greater concern is the appearance of entirely new species, some with toxins so potent that they have deadly consequences.

People living around the Pokomoke River in Maryland got a scare in 1997 when tens of thousands of dead fish began washing up on shore. The river is one of many that feeds into Chesapeake Bay on the East Coast of the States. The fish bodies were covered in sores; large chunks of flesh were missing as though something had taken a bite out of them. Then people working or playing in the water began to come down with headaches, stomach cramps and most frighteningly, loss of memory.

The culprit turned out to be *Pfiesteria* (rhymes with hysteria) *piscidia,* a tiny, single-cell organism that is part of a universe of microscopic creatures forming the base of the food web in the oceans. The group is known as dinoflagelates because they have long whip-like hairs that they flail around to move through the water. Pfiesteria has also been called the cell from hell because it changes its behaviour many times during its life cycle. Most of the time the little beasts float quietly in the calm, warm waters of rivers and estuaries like plants, acting as food for shellfish. But when they detect certain levels of excretions from fish, the microscopic menace performs a Jekyll and Hyde transformation. They begin to produce toxic chemicals that poison the fish and destroy their flesh. The microbes turn into carnivorous flesh-eating animals that consume the fish. The same toxins that Pfiesteria use to consume fish cause painful symptoms in humans.

When two more rivers were closed because of similar fish kills in Maryland, people panicked, and refused to eat seafood, which essentially shut down the billion-dollar industry for two months. Once the source of the mass infection was discovered, a debate broke out among scientists who argued whether or not the outbreak was caused by pollution. Dr. JoAnn Burkholder, a biologist from the University of Maryland, was most outspoken, suggesting that pollution running off the land from chicken and hog farms as well as sewage treatment plants provided the trigger that set off the outbreak. Nitrates, phosphates and other organics had been building up in the area for decades; it could have reached a critical point that pushed the Pfiesteria over the edge.

Scientists from the Woods Hole Oceanographic Institution disagreed, saying these blooms happen all the time as part of natural cycles in the sea. This one just happened to get a lot of attention. They also argue that we are seeing more algal blooms because of better scientific investigations looking for them. In 1984 there were twenty-two known dinoflagelates; now more than sixty have been identified. The organisms have always been there, we just didn't see them.

Eventually the Pfiesteria problem went away on its own and the debate over the role of pollution continues. But let's not forget that important corollary to the laws of Murphy, "If you push something hard enough, it will fall over."

There is no doubt that the oceans are getting warmer because of global climate change. Algae do better in warmer water. There is no doubt that the number of people living along coastlines has increased dramatically in the past decade which means more material is dumped in the water and more people can be affected by harmful algal blooms. One of the biggest hot spots is the Far East, where harbours in Hong Kong, Shanghai and Singapore are under increasing pressure from growing populations, populations that rely heavily on seafood. In 1998 a new species of red tide wiped out 75 percent of Hong Kong's farmed fish population, and another hit salmon farms on Vancouver Island.

Looked at globally, harmful algal blooms take on epidemic proportions, but this is not some new disease that has emerged out of the jungle; it's the impact of human activity on natural systems. Reduce our impact and the systems will recover. We don't need to use the oceans as a dumping ground.

At first sight the ocean seems boundless and clean, but spend some time on it and you can see the human influence. Far offshore, well out of sight of land, it's not uncommon to see discarded plastic containers floating by. That's not surprising when you look at the nautical charts for the East Coast. Huge rectangles covering hundreds of square kilometres are marked off as designated dumping grounds, where barges full of garbage are unloaded just over the horizon. In the Bahamas, where crystal-clear water laps against long-deserted beaches, plastic jugs, oil containers, disposable diapers and countless other throwaway articles litter the sand along the high-tide line. Plastic is everywhere.

You can even taste the human presence. The Atlantic doesn't really become comfortable to swim in until you get south of New York City but when you do jump in, watch out. The first time I swam in Chesapeake Bay I dove over the side of the boat and came up spitting. The water tasted metallic, like sucking on a nail. Later, when it was time to up the anchor, a black, foul-smelling muck clung to the anchor chain, dredged up from the bottom. I couldn't understand why people in restaurants were crazy about soft-shelled crab and shrimp that live on that bottom. I didn't eat any during the entire visit.

If Dr. Stephen Cunnane from the University of Toronto is right, we need shellfish if we want to stay smart. In 1999 he proposed a theory that it was eating shellfish that led to the development of the large human brain. He suggests that our evolution from tree-swinging jungle dwellers took a turn to the seashore where our diet shifted from a largely vegetarian menu to clams, mussels and oysters. Shellfish contain a chemical known as DHA which is very important for brain development in infants. That chemical is not found much in plant food. Shellfish also contain iodine, another form of brain food. If the theory that shellfish gave us big brains is true, it's a rather strange irony that today shellfish are poisoning us. In a way, we humans are like the toxic algae:

small in size but because of our numbers and ability to spread poisons, we affect large areas of the ocean.

Farther south along the coral reef just off the Florida Keys you see more signs of human influence on the ocean, "stuff" floating in the water. I'm not sure what it is, and having spent a lot of time swimming in that water I'm not sure I want to know, but it looks like snow slowly falling all the way to the bottom. And in keeping with the winter landscape in tropical paradise, the coral in the Florida Keys has been turning white, a disturbing process called bleaching. Living coral is coated with fungus that lives symbiotically. When the fungus dies the coral turns white. One scientist monitoring sea fans, the broad, leaf-shaped coral that looks like lace, has found the coral is dying so fast he has to check their condition three times a year. Normally coral takes hundreds of years to grow. The sea fans are dying from a fungal infection caused by a type of Aspergillus, normally found on land. The fungus usually appears in soil and is known for infecting the aged and people with weak immune systems, but now it has entered the ocean because of soil erosion. Up to 40 percent of the sea fans in the Florida Keys were infected in 1998.

Living coral is normally able to produce anti-fungal and anti-bacterial chemicals that offer protection against disease, but that system seems to be ineffective against this new invader. Bleaching is a problem throughout the Caribbean, especially during the El Niño years when ocean temperatures are higher. Exactly how extensive it will become, whether the coral will die off or if it's just a cycle the ocean passes through are questions no one has the answer to, but everyone involved in ocean studies is concerned.

It's hard to believe that creatures as small as humans can have such a profound effect on something as vast as the ocean. We've scooped the fish out with our nets, changed the chemistry and temperature of the water, introduced species where they don't belong; in many ways we have changed the face of the oceans as much as the land.

That said, efforts are under way to alleviate the impact of the infection called humanity, at least in North America. Local governments in the United States are now providing pumpouts at marinas. If the boaters would just install holding tanks, that problem would be solved. Canada has very strict standards for the quality of shellfish harvested in our own waters as well as those imported from other countries.

Outbreaks such as Pfiesteria have scared people living along the coast into environmental action, although controlling the runoff from agriculture is no easy task as farms become larger and more mechanized. Scientists are struggling to keep up with the new species of toxic algae to understand their life cycles, why they appear and the chemical makeup of their toxins so antidotes can be offered to lovers of seafood. Experiments in China have shown that simply dumping clay into the water gets rid of the algae by burying them in the bottom sediment. Perhaps there is hope for the oceans yet.

All this talk of pollution can get pretty depressing but most days spent sailing on the open ocean are glorious.

There may be frost at the north and south poles of the Moon, permafrost on Mars and maybe even an ocean under the permanent ice cover on Europa, a moon of Jupiter, but there is no other place that we know of where the sound of surf can be heard. Our oceans seem vast but in fact they form just a thin film around the planet. Dip a basketball underwater then pull it out again. The water that clings to the ball is about the same thickness as the oceans are to the Earth, a thin film around a rocky ball.

After sailing up and down the East Coast, we followed a short-cut back to the Great Lakes by way of the Hudson River, past the unbelievable skyline of Manhattan to upstate New York. With the help of the friendly staff at the Hop 'O Nose Marina, the masts were lowered and lashed to the decks. Then it was off for three days of motoring along the Erie Barge Canal climbing through thirty-two locks along the way to Lake Ontario. The sight of our fresh-water sea was, to say the least, refreshing. Once I had cleaned the brown river water scum line off the bow, we crossed the lake to the Canadian side and dropped anchor near the beach of Presqu'ile Park, not far from Kingston. As the boat settled back on her line for the night I called to my partner, "Sandy, come here quick!"

She raced up to join me on the bow, worried that something was wrong.

"Look at that!" I said pointing at the water.

"What, I don't see anything!" she replied rather confused.

"The anchor, you can see it lying on the bottom!"

For the first time in weeks the water was clear enough for us to see the anchor embedded in the sand. We stood there amazed that Lake Ontario water actually looked clean compared to what we had been sailing in. The Great Lakes really are a precious gem on the face of the Earth.

There is a long way to go in our cleanup of water but it is an entirely doable task. That's the remarkable thing about H_2O, it can be cleaned up. If it didn't have that capacity we would have run out of it a long time ago. The water we drink today is probably almost as old as the Earth itself. When the planet was young, water gushed out of thousands of volcanoes as steam and rained down on the surface for millennia. More water may have come from space as icy comets slammed into the atmosphere. But most of that bombardment from above and eruptions from below subsided after a billion years or so. Since then the same water has been used over and over and over again through the cleansing process of the water cycle. Evaporation, condensation, precipitation lifts water from the ground to the sky and back again, a remarkable process that removes impurities every time. The water that fills your drinking glass today was sipped by dinosaurs. There's one for the dinner table . . .

If the water cycle was not in place the water on Earth would have become permanently contaminated early on, possibly preventing the emergence of life. It's remarkable that a simple molecule, dihydrous oxide, two hydrogen atoms stuck to an oxygen atom, is so durable, so common and so precious.

Water's ability to endure means it will survive future millennia, it's just a matter of whether it will remain palatable to us. Water will be THE issue in the twenty-first century, hopefully a global dream, not just for our own survival, but for the sake of those who live within the liquid drop that coats this planet.

BRETHREN BELOW

Poison failed, so now we're loving
the whales to death

ROLLING NIGHT WATERS ARE blacker than the night sky. At least stars illuminate the cosmos. City lights twinkle along the shoreline but the liquid hissing past the hull is a cold, bottomless void. Night vision is almost nonexistent, forcing my brain to ignore the lack of depth perception and assess our position offshore. I feel like an alien visiting a strange environment when all of a sudden one of the local residents, sensing my presence, makes contact.

A few metres off to the left and slightly behind the stern railing I hear a breath, an exhalation bursting from the water like a punctured tire. My first thought is something has fallen off the boat, but the sound is not that of a splash, it's a quick rush of air that ends as abruptly as it begins. I look out and see nothing in the inky blackness. Another burst, this time closer to the boat. I catch a brief glimpse of spray and a quick flash of light reflecting off a shiny surface. The burst of air is followed by a gasp, then silence. No piece of flotsam from a boat sounds like that and my brain, under enough strain to grasp reality in this aquatic world of darkness, finally grapples with the fact that a dolphin is swimming beside the boat.

No matter what you've seen of whales and dolphins in

aquatic theme parks or seaquariums, nothing prepares you for a close encounter with these animals in the wild. Their arrival is always a surprise, their curiosity brings them very close and if you are in a sailboat, their swimming ability far exceeds your top speed, so they voluntarily come to check you out, you don't visit them.

In the darkness of Puget Sound, I could barely make out the shape of the sleek dark body gliding along just beneath the surface. The top of its head broke the smooth surface briefly, just long enough for another one-second exhale, spray and inhale before slipping beneath the surface with barely a ripple. It was cruising effortlessly alongside the boat, matching speed and course exactly. There were none of the chirps and whistles so familiar in the captive animals; obviously there was no reason to make noise—it was a wild animal scouting its territory, checking out the hull passing through the water. I've heard that whales, dolphins and porpoises approach sailboats more than other vessels because the rounded shape of a hull with its protruding keel slipping through the water without sound resembles a whale swimming on its back. Perhaps they approach to find out why a whale would choose to swim upside down; I'm not sure, but I have been fortunate to experience many visitations by these remarkable cousins of ours that live beneath the waves.

There was something astounding about that first encounter at night on the Pacific coast off Seattle: this creature, about the same size as me, breathing the same air and a distant relative on the same evolutionary family tree, was perfectly comfortable in total darkness swimming through frigid water just a few degrees above freezing, water that would kill me in about fifteen minutes if I was to fall into it. It's hard to believe we live on the same planet, let alone that we are related to each other.

While I don't completely agree with keeping animals in

captivity, especially those that range over large territories, aquariums do provide an opportunity to see these animals up close. I've been fortunate to get extremely up close with captives thanks to the education staff of Marineland in Niagara Falls. I was a staff member in the education department of the Ontario Science Centre at the time and we were on an exchange visit to share ideas about communicating science to the public. The day before the chief instructor called to say, "Bring your bathing suits."

Before the gates open to the public, the aquarium staff are busy feeding the animals and checking equipment. The animals are alert and active, like a family gathering for breakfast. We changed into our bathing suits and were led into a large indoor pool where six performing dolphins swam lazily in endless circles. It's impressive enough to stand on the edge of the pool looking down on these animals, who were also looking up at us but when the instructor said, "Go ahead, jump in!" I wasn't prepared for the intensity of meeting these creatures on their own turf.

The first and most overwhelming sensation, other than the coldness of the water, was sound. A cacophony of squeals, clicks and grunts echoed throughout the pool as the dolphins began flitting about in all directions. They were held captive in a relatively small area, now their limited space was being invaded further by human bodies in the water with them. Through my mask I could see their incredibly swift and deft manoeuvres racing to the far side, then rushing swiftly past just out of arm's reach. This was no encounter with Flipper, the happy little dolphin with an altruistic attitude towards humanity. These animals were clearly agitated and didn't want me in their pool. The instructor reached down, handed me a fish and said, "The only way they'll come near you is if you have food in your hand."

I swam out to the centre of the pool and held the fish out as an offering. No way. They approached but didn't take, like pigeons in a park looking for a handout but constantly wary of approaching too close. The frantic swimming and squealing continued for a few more minutes before I wanted out. It felt too uncomfortable being the source of such agitation; besides, I was getting cold. These animals don't need heated pools. I've always thought of myself as a reasonably strong swimmer but compared to the high-speed underwater ballet happening around me I felt like a tortoise on land as I slogged my way back to the poolside. Stranger in an alien environment indeed.

Back on the deck watching them calm down, I wanted to apologize for causing such a disturbance. Too bad we haven't broken through that language barrier. Since that encounter I shudder whenever I see advertisements from hotels in the tropics offering a chance to swim with dolphins. I've seen these places where the animals are corralled into a shallow fenced area around a beach so tourists can surround the dolphins and run their suntan-lotioned hands over the animals' bodies. I feel fortunate to have the more pleasurable and decent experience of meeting these animals in the wild, where the encounter is their choice not ours.

Years later, during one particularly brilliant day under sail in the Bahamas we had a marvellous encounter with a family of six bottlenose dolphins, including a baby, when they decided to use the bow wave of the boat as an amusement ride. Effortlessly keeping up with our leisurely pace, the animals darted back and forth from one side of the boat to the other, their dorsal fins mere centimetres away from the hull. The baby swam in perfect synchrony close beside its mother through the crystal-clear water. A boat creates a pressure wave around the bow as it ploughs through the water and dolphins surf along getting a free ride by simply holding their bodies close to the hull. One animal seemed to be showing off its skill by turning upside down with its fins along either side of the bow as though giving the boat a hug. After frolicking on the bow wave the whole family came alongside close to where we were standing in the cockpit. Then while matching speed with the boat they rolled on their side, each raised one eye out of the water and looked at us. It's a deliberate act, a position they hold for several seconds as though they are saying hello, or who are you? Who knows what goes through those large brains. For a few moments during this brief encounter, this planet of ours seemed a little larger with a much more varied population.

Relating to dolphins is somewhat easy because they have bodies about the same size as ours, but whales are another game altogether, and one of the best places to see them is the lower St. Lawrence River.

Downstream from Quebec City, where the river becomes so wide that the shorelines are almost out of sight of each other, the St. Lawrence is joined by another large river, the Saguenay, which cuts an impressive gorge through the Laurentians. The town of Tadoussac on the north shore stands at a unique junction where the two massive flows pour into each other then swirl on the tides from the gulf. At this juncture the waters are alive with eddy currents and upwellings from the deep. Just getting into Tadoussac harbour is a challenge for a sailboat. The entrance is guarded by a line of frothing, standing waves 2 metres high driven by currents so powerful they are only passable on a rising tide. The whole area is the small end of a giant funnel. The shorelines converge from the open sea while the floor of the river rises from a depth of 335 metres to less than 40 metres in a very short distance, a huge underwater hill, possibly the remnant of an ice age waterfall. The funnelling effect of the geography concentrates deep-water nutrients and plankton, which are swept up to the surface along the face of the underwater hill and focused into a small section of the river, making it a prime feeding site for whales and a prime whale-watching site for humans.

Every year blue, fin and minke whales along with the occasional humpback and even sperm whale come to the area to take advantage of the bountiful harvest. And swimming among the giants are the local residents of these waters, the snow-white belugas. At first glance belugas look like whitecaps on the water, but there is no foam, and the whiteness is so pure it's almost blinding.

We don't often see large animals close up which makes an encounter with a whale in the wild a magical experience. It's hard to believe that we are related to these somewhat alien-looking creatures who are totally comfortable in cold, dark water where humans would perish in minutes. Hearts beat in their chests, brains larger than our own socialize with others of their own kind.

You don't really see whales in the wild, you just see pieces of them, although belugas shine through the water more because of their pure white skin. When you are in whale territory your eyes strain to see details along the surface of the water. The first sighting is almost always out of the corner of your eye, a quick flash of a white crescent that appears like a ghost then vanishes as quickly as you turn your head. But once you've spotted an animal there is a good chance you will see it a second time. That tells you the direction it's swimming, which you hope is the same as your direction. Usually it's not and that is the end of your experience with that animal. But occasionally your paths will cross and you have the privilege to witness the silent passage of these docile animals. There is no splashing or even a wake as they glide through the water. Bulbous heads approach the surface with a line of large bubbles trailing from their blowholes. The top of the head briefly touches the air while a burst of spray announces a big exhalation followed by a quick gasp inwards. "Booshshsh . . . shup!" In less than a second the breath is complete, the back arches like a sickle smoothly cutting the water and the animal returns to the deep.

Belugas are among the smaller members of the whale family, only about seven metres long. But they have become the symbol for pollution in the waters of the St. Lawrence. Perhaps it is their pure white colour that makes them seem more susceptible to the stains of our waste products, but when belugas began washing up on shore, their blubber loaded with toxins, they triggered an environmental cleanup that has preserved some populations from extinction.

Belugas were swimming in the St. Lawrence during the last ice age twelve thousand years ago. Their numbers plunged from twenty thousand down to five thousand by the turn of the century thanks to hunting and they were almost completely eradicated in the twenties and thirties when the Quebec government offered a bounty on the animals in response to fishermen who complained that belugas were stealing their catch. By 1979, when hunting was finally banned, only a few hundred remained and were immediately put on the endangered species list. Since then the beluga population has made a small comeback with the numbers somewhere around a thousand, depending on whom you ask. It's difficult to get an accurate population count on animals that spend much of their time below the surface.

But the human onslaught of belugas is not over. During the eighties the white whales began washing up on shore, their bodies loaded with an alphabet of toxic chemicals: PCBs, DDT, PAHs and lead. One-fifth of them had intestinal cancer, a rate higher than all other species including humans. Clearly, the animals had succumbed to the outpourings of all those factories I had passed along the shores of the Great Lakes and St. Lawrence River. The levels of toxic chemicals were so high they exceeded government standards for shipping. In other words, the whales should have special permits for transporting hazardous waste down the river.

Belugas of the St. Lawrence are more susceptible to contamination because unlike the other whales who migrate in from the ocean every year, they live in the area year round which gives them greater exposure to polluted water. They also eat fish, which accumulate toxins on their own. So even if the chemicals are at low levels in the water, they are concentrated in animals higher up on the food chain, a process called biomagnification. By the time you get to the whales at the top of the chain, belugas are getting quite a high dose of toxins every time they take a meal. Those same toxins are expressed in the whales' milk so baby belugas begin life on a diet of poison.

The future of the St. Lawrence belugas looked bleak, but they have one saving grace that is as much responsible for their survival as their physical strength: they're cute. There's something about button eyes on a bulbous white head with a permanent smile that gives belugas tremendous public appeal. Other whales may be majestic, but cute wins every time in the poster contest. Baby seals benefit from the same appeal.

That high public profile of the white whales prompted quick action, resulting in stiffer government regulations and industrial co-operation. Saving whales makes everyone look good. Corny or not, the plight of the whales produced dramatic improvements in water quality. PCBs have been banned, other chemicals reduced more than 90 percent. It will still take years for the toxins to leave the whales' bodies because blubber is a very good warehouse for toxins, but at least now they have a fighting chance.

I had the opportunity to meet two scientists currently working to determine just how close to the edge of survival the white whales are. Robert Michaud, a charismatic young researcher, has been getting to know the belugas literally by name since 1985. Both Robert and the animals live in the area year round so he has identified more than a hundred individuals by distinctive cuts and gashes on their fins and tails. But he couldn't tell the difference between the boys and the girls.

Michaud wants to understand why the animals are not increasing in numbers since hunting has been banned and food is plentiful. Perhaps the toxins from the pollution have affected their reproduction. When a population is reduced to very small numbers, close relatives are forced to mate, reducing the size of the gene pool. Scientists call this a genetic bottleneck. Without genetic diversity the extended family is more susceptible to disease or the effects of pollution. A small, inbred group can pass disease around like the family cold, where one person gets an infection then everyone comes down with it.

To find out who is related to whom Robert hunted the whales with a crossbow. A small dart removes a tiny piece of skin from each whale, then a biopsy in the lab reveals the genetic makeup, sex of the animals and level of toxic contamination in their bodies.

The early results showed Robert that many names he had given to the whales were the wrong gender. He is rewriting the list of names and trying to establish the relationships. He has also found several clans of animals and wants to know how the groups relate to each other. Fortunately, there is quite a bit of genetic diversity, although the St. Lawrence whales are distinct and isolated from other beluga populations living in the Arctic. That means if they are wiped out, they probably won't be replaced. Only time will tell.

The most encouraging finding of all the studies of the St. Lawrence belugas is that their numbers seem to be holding steady, although why they are not on the increase is still a mystery.

Meanwhile, yet another in the long list of human assaults on the whales' survival has emerged, this time from people who are almost loving them to death.

Whale-watching is a worldwide growth industry bringing in hundreds of millions of tourist dollars annually. As soon as we entered the Tadoussac area our quiet sail down the river became a busy run through traffic as we were surrounded by vessels of all sizes. Large tour boats with platforms extending beyond the bow crammed with camera-carrying tourists, small zodiacs buzzing about, their yellow-rainsuited passengers holding on tightly as the craft bounced over the waves, and in the centre of all this activity, a lone whale, completely surrounded by gawking humans.

The industry is growing so fast and without regulations that the Quebec government convened a conference in 1998 to bring conservationists and tour operators together to figure out how to keep the tourist industry alive without killing the whales.

It was an interesting gathering for three days, with presentations and group discussions from all fronts. A representative from Tourisme Québec showed a very persuasive video featuring whale-watching as the main reason to come to the province. He did everything but rub his hands with glee over the annual bounty brought to the area by 300,000 tourists who spent $7 million in fares and $51 million in food, lodging, transportation and souvenirs. He almost drooled over the prospects of even more money for the government in the near future. Conservationists were worried about the inevitable increase in tourist traffic as the reputation of the area spreads. More tourists means more demand for boats. Pictures taken from the air showed as many as fifty boats surrounding a small pod of whales during peak season. The tour operators claimed their presence doesn't bother the whales at all. I was expecting it to be a free-for-all debate but everyone was actually quite respectful of the others' needs.

All agreed that keeping the whales healthy is in everyone's best interests and keeping the number of boats on the water to a reasonable number provides the best experience for the visitors. The question was how to manage the area so everyone's needs are met.

The first step towards conservation was declaring the area a marine sanctuary. That means government control over fishing and tourist activities. The next point was easy for everyone to agree on, that beluga whales are strictly off limits unless they happen to pass by the boat on their own. Belugas have a habit of approaching boats out of curiosity, which is fine because whales are allowed to people-watch. But with only a thousand animals in the population they don't need the pressure of being chased.

Overall, the belugas have already changed their behaviour because of the presence of humans. Tadoussac harbour was once a feeding and breeding ground but now it has been abandoned because of a new marina and heavy boat traffic.

Conservationists are concerned that the presence of boats can interfere with breeding, separate mothers from calves and generally tire the animals out.

Peter Sheifele gave a different perspective on the whole scene, the view from underwater. Peter is a bioacoustic researcher at the University of Connecticut who studies underwater sounds. His skill comes from a career in the navy where he identified ships by the sounds of their propellers, an important skill in hunting down unfriendly visitors. He happened to be in Tadoussac on other business and out of curiosity tossed his hydrophone over the side of his boat to listen in on any whale chatter. He was astounded at the noise that came thundering through his earphones. Merchant ships chugging up the St. Lawrence River, outboard motors, even the sound of music from people playing radios on pleasure boats. It was one of the loudest marine environments he had ever heard. And he's been in a lot of places. That prompted him to join Robert Michaud's team to survey the area and measure the levels of sound the whales are exposed to every day. I was invited to accompany them on one of their surveys.

We headed up the Saguenay Fjord, a spectacular, steep-walled valley that cuts through the Laurentians. Robert knows the location of a beluga feeding ground that is off limits to tour boats. A pod of about a dozen belugas splashed around a small bay, the most whales I've ever seen in one place. We kept our distance because sound travels so well underwater that the hydrophone can pick up noises from many kilometres away.

I was looking forward to hearing the chirps, squeaks and whistles from their chattering language, but when the microphone was lowered over the side and Peter put the headphones on my head, the only sound I heard was a loud chug, chug, chug like an old steam locomotive running up a steep hill.

"What's that?" I ask in surprise.

"Over there," he points.

About two kilometres away a tanker ship steams upriver. Even with binoculars it's too far away to identify any markings, yet through the hydrophone it sounds like we are on an immediate collision course. Peter takes the headset, listens for a few seconds then announces, "Single screw, four-bladed propeller." He presses the earphones against his head, listening to the pulsating sound, then continues, "And one of the blades has a nick or bend in it."

"How do you know that?" I ask.

"I used to work in the navy as an acoustic engineer. It was my job to identify ships by their sound."

A large propeller churning through the water creates air bubbles, a process called cavitation which is actually the water being torn apart by the force of the blade. The bubbles generate a sound that is unique to every propeller. Peter can identify different types of ships and even name individual vessels just by their sounds.

Somewhere, lost in the distant background of all that noise, the shrill squeals and clicks come from the whales, sounds that once dominated these waters. Whale biologists worry about the effect all that noise is having on the whales' hearing. The low-frequency, pounding noises coming from dozens of large ships that plough up and down the river every day carry a great deal of energy.

"Any animal that uses its hearing to navigate underwater and search for food will suffer from damage to its ears," Peter said. "A deaf whale is a dead whale as far as I'm concerned."

But even though scientists like Peter Sheifele and Robert

Michaud have raised concerns about the effect of underwater noise and the presence of boats, it's difficult to test for these effects on wild animals. You can't give them earphones and ask them to take a hearing test. So while the scientists are raising red flags, all the science hasn't been done to back them up, which is the ammunition used by the tour operators who claim their boats do no harm.

To get the other side of the story we hire a small zodiac for a few hours and set out with one of the experienced tour guides. All we ask is to see some whales.

Two one-hundred-horsepower outboards on the back of an inflatable boat get you across the water at frightening speeds, especially for a sailor like me who is used to cruising along under wind power at about the speed of a bicyclist. The tour guide knows exactly where to go after many years of experience in these waters and he didn't waste any time leaping over whitecaps to get us there.

His first target is a brown line in the water formed between tidal and river currents. At first I think it's another ugly sign of human pollution but as we slow down and drift along the line I realize that the line is alive. With the palm of my hand I scoop up dozens of miniature shrimp, the famous krill that are the staple food of baleen whales. The animals are so small you have to look closely to see their shape. Countless billions of them darken the water in a line stretching several kilometres in both directions. "Whale food," says the guide. "Minke whales feed along this line."

There are two other types of whale food in the area, capelan, a small species of fish and phytoplankton, which are microscopic plants. Each is at a different depth in the water. Krill are usually found deeper down but they had been brought to the surface here by the incoming tide rushing up the large underwater hill.

It didn't take long, drifting with the engine idling, for one of us to make the first sighting of a black dorsal fin and dark body arching through the brown line. Minke are not much bigger than dolphins, with a reputation for being camera shy because they are very hard to photograph. Instead of swimming more or less in a straight line, they dodge back and forth, so if you see a fin once, you don't know where to look for it the second time.

Suddenly, out of nowhere, three other boats join us, one of them a two-hundred-passenger catamaran. Tour guides squawk on loudspeakers while tourists crowding the rail squeal with delight . . . forget the noises underwater, there is a cacophony of sound above the surface as well. A crackle on the radio alerts our driver. He has a short conversation in French with another captain then announces, "That boat way out there on the horizon has a fin whale, do you want to go see it?"

We unanimously agree and with a roar of the big engines we blast out of the krill-laden waters like a space shuttle leaving the pad. We cross two or three kilometres of water in minutes.

To say that fin whales are big is a gross understatement. They are massive, forty to fifty tonnes of flesh the length of a locomotive. Their size is seconded only by the much rarer blue whale, the largest animal to ever live. Smaller belugas or minke are like galloping horses; you can see their bodies moving up and down as they swim by, their arched backs appearing for just a second or two before they dip back down beneath the surface. Big whales are awesome to see, especially from a small boat. It takes a long time for the animal to go by.

Our seasoned guide makes the first sighting of spray from the fin whale's blowhole, just off the bow of another large tour boat about half a kilometre away. He watches carefully, then calmly turns our boat back in the direction we came and slowly putters to a spot on the open water.

"We'll wait here for about fifteen minutes," he says leaning back in his chair to light a cigarette. I begin to wonder if this is some kind of scam where they get you out on the water and waste a lot of time just drifting around before taking you to where the whales really are.

"Isn't the whale over there?" I ask.

"It just took a dive so it won't be up for about fifteen minutes. When it comes back it should surface right about here."

The guide explained how the big whales like the fin and blue swim in very large circles when they feed, so the trick is trying to predict where they will surface after the dive and just be there when the whale comes up. Hopefully it comes up right next to the boat. Tour operators are not supposed to chase the whales, but they can place themselves in the whales' path. Since the animals are approaching the boats in that situation, the boats are not technically harassing the animals. The line seems pretty thin to me.

Nonetheless, I was impressed by our guide's skill in predicting the behaviour of the whale, for no sooner had fifteen minutes passed than a powerful geyser burst about ten metres off our stern. The first sighting is always a glance but it's enough to know that the living locomotive is coming our way and it's moving fast. The guide puts the engines in gear but doesn't touch the throttles. Slowly he turns the boat parallel to the whale's course.

"It will surface three or four more times before diving again, so keep looking to the right."

The only big whales I've seen are skeletons and models hanging in museums, which give some sense of the size, but not the mass of these mighty creatures. One of the best artists who sculpts those life-sized models is Dr. Paul Brodie, a whale biologist formerly with the Bedford Institute of Oceanography. He's the only sculptor I know who is also a scientist. His life-size carvings of whales are both a hobby and an aid to studying the animals. "You don't understand something until you try to build it," he told me while surrounded by wooden moulds and fibreglass resin that cluttered his workshop. He showed me the fine curves of a whale's body, how it tapers to an incredibly thin sliver before broadening out to form the tail. "Isn't it amazing how all the power to drive an animal weighing fifty or sixty tonnes comes through this one narrow joint?" he says with a true sense of awe in his voice.

Dr. Brodie spent years on whaling ships dissecting the animals to probe their inner workings. He was always on call so whenever a large whale became stranded on shore he could pursue his study of whale muscles and organs. One question that bothered him as a scientist was how a whale manages to open and close its mouth underwater and still capture its food. A whale's mouth is like a bucket: once it fills with water, nothing more goes in. If you try catching fish with a bucket it doesn't work because you end up pushing the fish ahead of the bucket rather than trapping them inside. It's easy for the fish to escape around the rim of the bucket even if it's moving through the water. That's why nets have holes in them so the water can pass right through but the fish can't. The whales obviously have some trick to get around this problem.

Dr. Brodie discovered the whale's secret using huge, steam-powered jacks which he mounted around freshly dissected jawbones removed from a fin whale. The idea was to simply move the bones through the entire opening and closing action just to see how they work.

He found that the fifteen-metre-long bones, which make up a third of the animal's body, actually dislocate from the jaw when the whale's mouth opens allowing the lower lip to point straight down, ninety degrees from the rest of the head. Loose skin in the throat balloons out like a giant parachute, bringing the animal to an almost complete stop in the water. What Dr. Brodie wanted to know was how the whale manages to engulf a school of krill and keep the prey in the centre of the mouth while the huge jaws close around it.

The answer came when his steam-powered jawbones reached their fully open position. A loud popping noise came from the joints. They were cracking like giant knuckles. The sound travels along the jawbones where it is amplified and focused towards the centre of the mouth opening. The sudden pop startles the prey which cluster into a ball in the whale's throat, a reflex that lasts just long enough for the enormous mouth to close around them. Then a tongue the size of a sofa pushes several hundred litres of water up through baleen plates lining the jaw. The plates act as filters allowing the water to pass through but trap the krill. Then I guess the whale just goes "gulp."

I tried to imagine that whole sequence happening to the animal that was fast approaching our little boat. Even after seeing many of Dr. Brodie's full-scale models I wasn't prepared for the majesty of these animals in the wild.

A gnarled snout emerges from the black water just a few metres off the right-hand side of our boat. It's moving fast, the leading edge of a living torpedo. More of the head appears, sporting a large knob rising out of the top with two holes resembling nostrils pointed backwards, the distinctive double blowhole of a fin whale. The instant the blowhole breaks the surface a whoosh of spray shoots ten metres into the air along with a strong hiss. Five hundred litres of air escapes from the breathing hole at about 300 km/h as the gigantic lungs deflate. A quick gasp sucks in an equal amount of air down through the big windpipes which seal themselves off just before the blowhole slides beneath the surface. All that air has been exchanged in less than half a second.

The wind is blowing away from us so we don't get to smell the whale breath, which I must say I'm not too disappointed about, but the show is not over yet. We have only seen the head. The rest of the animal still has to swim by. By the time a beluga would have come and gone the body of the fin whale has yet to emerge fully from the water. The arching form of the black streamlined body rises upwards like an enormous inner tube rolling through the water. One, two, three seconds go by and the massive shape is still passing. We are only seeing a small part of the entire animal and it still looks huge—the visible portion alone is larger than our boat. We are clearly in the presence of something very, very big, yet so smooth that barely a ripple disturbs the water. A sickle-shaped dorsal fin emerges following a long curving path over the arching body, then cleanly slices back down under the surface. Finally, the shadowy form of a broad flat tail the size of a small airplane wing glides silently by just below the surface. As quickly as it appeared it vanishes, leaving a round pool of smooth water swirling where the activity had been. To the whale it was just another single breath, to us it was a close encounter with the second largest animal on the planet.

The perspective from a small boat only metres away from the great whale is as close as you can get to a big whale without actually diving in the water. We see the animal rise to the surface three more times as it cruises along almost effortlessly ahead of us. From behind we can see the undulating motion of the long body where the entire surfacing action is completed with one long stroke of the tail. On the final appearance the back arches a little higher and the whale returns to the darkness below for another meal.

As we stand there dumbfounded, grinning madly at each other, our proud tour guide says, "See, we didn't disturb that whale, it didn't change its course, it didn't care about us at all." He is right: we certainly seemed like insignificant flotsam floating on the surface while the whale went about its business. But another study by Robert Michaud tells a different story.

Every year boats and the gentle giants collide, sometimes with fatal results. Propeller scars cut across the backs of the animals are evidence of at least two collisions per year. All are unintentional, but when too many boats gather to see the whales, the confusion of manoeuvring to stay out of each other's way can place the boats in a circle surrounding the animal which cuts off its path.

Michaud's concern, however, goes beyond collisions. He is interested in how the mere presence of boats affects the diving behaviour of whales. In a unique experiment using temporary radio transmitters attached by suction to the backs of twenty-five fin whales, he was able to track their dives and see how they behaved while out of sight below the surface. Between 1994 and '96 he tracked more than 2,500 dives and found that indeed there is a difference when boats are around.

Whales alternate between swimming along the surface of the water and feeding at depths up to 150 metres. Their surface time of course is for breathing which they do in a series of four or five shallow dives lasting only a minute or two each. This is prime whale-watching time because the multiple blows allow many opportunities to see the animal from a boat. When enough oxygen has been exchanged through the lungs, the whale arches its back, and the tail may rise entirely out of the water—the photo opportunity everyone hopes for—then it plunges into the deep where it remains submerged for twelve to fifteen minutes.

Michaud found that the whales stay near the surface at night and dive deeply only during the day. Their dives have two different forms. One is a "V" dive where the animal basically goes straight down and straight back up again. Such dives are performed just before dawn, possibly as surveying dives to locate the food. Once the Sun comes up the whale changes to "U" dives, where it spends more time at depth. This is believed to be the prime feeding time.

The researchers found somewhat to their surprise that the fin whales take just as many shallow breathing dives at the surface whether there are boats around or not, which the tour operators were delighted to hear. The more disturbing result showed that whales spend fewer minutes feeding on the bottom when there are boats around, which translates into less food going into the whales' mouths. Whether that's because they're not gathering enough of a breath on the surface is hard to tell. That also meant the whales makes more dives in a day which is a greater output of energy for the same amount of food. At least that's the theory. Since fin whales are migratory, it's difficult to know what effect this has on their health once they leave the area. Robert Michaud is concerned that fin whales, like other large migratory whales, may not feed for months at a time during migration and breeding. The tour operators said there isn't conclusive information.

By the end of the three-day meeting no hard regulations had been established for whale-watching conduct. They would be hard to enforce anyway with only one park patrol boat available. Everyone did agree to a code of ethics where they will remain two hundred metres distant and enforce a self-policing policy. There was talk of creating zones within the park and controlling traffic within the zones by special permits. Selected beluga feeding areas would be off limits, with other locations reserved for whale-watching from land. But the tour operators didn't like this idea because the whales follow the food. If they gather in one zone, only boats with permits for that zone will see them while everyone else is left out. All tour operators promise their customers whales on every trip.

As we saw on our little adventure, co-operating with the other boats and placing themselves in the path of the whales is still a common practice. Unfortunately, it also brings the best results for happy tourists. The industry is expected to grow by 10 percent a year. The good news is that there is no indication the whale population is declining, but there is no proof that it's growing either. Time will certainly tell.

Leaving Tadoussac for the Gulf of St. Lawrence, we felt fortunate to be sailing in our own boat. It provides the luxury of encountering the whales in an almost one-on-one environment. Most sightings are at a distance, although one pod of half a dozen pilot whales passed within a few metres of the bow while we sailed past Ingonnish beach along the top end of Cape Breton Island. The small black whales look like they're wearing motorcycle helmets as their round, shiny black heads bob out of the water each time they take a breath. It seems like they are taking a look around. Perhaps they are.

The depths these animals dive are unfathomable to most of us, except the person who has been deeper in the ocean than even the whales can go.

Part Three
Terra (In)Firma

CRACKED EGGS AND EARTHQUAKES

*A contagious passion for
the Earth's crust*

"Do you like my new barn?"

The tall, lanky fellow, with a carpenter's belt slung low around his waist like a holster, faces the brand new unpainted barn that dominates the property. He is covered head to foot in sawdust.

"Yes," I reply, "Its a very fine barn."

I have just driven a thousand kilometres to New England hoping to do an interview with a scientist. I wasn't expecting to meet a barn builder. He stands with a hammer in one hand and a triangular piece of wood in the other, marvelling at his new creation. He hasn't said hello.

"It's almost finished. This is the last piece," he grins, holding up the small chunk of wood. Then he disappears back into the barn. I begin to wonder if I have the right place. The instructions given over the phone have led me to a farm on Cape Cod where I am supposed to meet a geologist from the Woods Hole Oceanographic Institution who has made some exciting new discoveries at the bottom of the ocean. This guy seems to be more interested in his barn.

A few hard knocks from a hammer ring out from inside the structure, then he reappears minus the piece of wood, stands in the same spot again facing his masterpiece, spreads his arms and declares, "There, it's done."

"Congratulations." I didn't know what else to say.

I am about to ask if he knows of a scientist who lives nearby but he marches right past me, still without a hello, and disappears into the farmhouse. I grab the page of instructions out of my car and read them again. Moments later he emerges carrying two glasses and a bottle of wine. Walking past me again, he says, "Let's do the interview in my new barn."

I follow him up into the empty loft where he opens the big upper doors, revealing a typical Cape Cod scene of swaying grass waving in the warm spring breezes. The wine cork pops, we toast his new barn, then, framed by the pastoral Cape Cod scenery amid the scent of spring flowers and freshly cut wood, we proceed with one of the most enjoyable and informative interviews I've ever done. Such was my introduction to Dr. Robert Ballard.

In the world of science, where few experts are able to see beyond scientific facts and communicate through stories and vivid images, Robert Ballard is one of the poets. Outlandishly funny, he doesn't fit the stereotypical image of the scientist. He speaks with such passion for his subject that you can't help but be drawn in by his charm.

Most of Ballard's career as a geologist has been spent exploring the bottom of the deep ocean. Crammed into small, specially designed submarines capable of withstanding the tons of pressure four kilometres below the surface, he was among the first to see what others had only theorized about, huge cracks in the crust of the Earth that run under all the oceans of the world. The giant fissures are both the birthplace and the graveyard for the ever-changing face of our planet.

That afternoon in the barn was an inspirational day. His descriptions of the geologist's point of view have stuck with me more than any images described by anyone else. He told me how the Earth would feel squishy beneath your feet if your were a giant walking along the surface, because the crust of our planet actually floats on a liquid layer underneath. He described a geologist's perception of time, where a million years is merely an instant and how it takes a hundred million years just to see things happen.

"Do you remember the movie *The Time Machine?*" he asked.

"An inventive scientist living in the 1800s develops a machine that can move through time while remaining in the same location. The inventor sits behind the controls of his machine and watches the scene out his workshop window change as he travels through time towards the future. The dress on a mannequin in a storefront across the street changes. The hemline gets longer, then shorter, then cars appear, new buildings, then flying machines; finally as he accelerates even faster through time, millions of years begin flashing by. An ice age comes and goes, volcanoes appear, until he sees the Earth itself evolving before his eyes.

"People think of the Earth as dead and unmoving but that's just because we haven't been around long enough to watch it change. It's like a butterfly sitting on the branch of a giant sequoia tree. The butterfly lives for a few days, the sequoia tree lives for a couple of thousand years. If you were to ask the butterfly if he perceives the tree as alive, the butterfly would say 'No, I've been here all my life and the tree hasn't done a damn thing.' We don't see the Earth change because we don't live long enough, but when you look at it in the sped-up time-lapse version covering millions of years, it's alive. That's how I see the Earth."

Ballard's work exploring the giant cracks in the bottom of the ocean was to find evidence for a relatively new theory that has revolutionized the science of geology. It's called plate tectonics and basically says that the surface of the Earth is broken into about a dozen continent-sized pieces called plates. All of North America is one plate, the floor of the Pacific Ocean is another. These plates shift around like pieces of a jigsaw puzzle, changing the face of the Earth. Two hundred and thirty million years ago all the continents were huddled together in to one large supercontinent called Pangea. The rest of the world was covered by one huge ocean called Panthalassa. With only one continent and one ocean the climate of the Earth was quite different from what we see today; heat was able to circulate more easily around the globe. Most of Pangea was a dry desert almost all the way to the South Pole. There were no ice caps in the Arctic or Antarctica. Earth was a much warmer place. Once Pangea broke up, about the time of the dinosaurs, the continents spread apart, breaking up the great ocean into smaller sections, cutting off the global flow of heat and lowering temperatures.

If Dr. Paul Hoffman is right, the cooling of the planet could have triggered the ultimate ice age. The Harvard scientist suggested in 1999 that when both the South Pole was covered by the continent of Antarctica and the North Pole was surrounded by land, warm water from the tropics couldn't reach the polar areas so they froze over, chilling the Earth much like toes sticking out the bottom of a blanket make you feel chilly on a cold night in bed. The growing ice caps stole water from the oceans so sea levels dropped, exposing more land for snow to accumulate on. As more land became covered in snow, the Earth became whiter, reflecting sunlight back into space, sunlight that would have brought heat to that land. There is some evidence that this whitening of the Earth ran out of control until the whole planet froze, right down to the equator . . . a snowball Earth. Dr. Hoffman says this was not just a one-time fluke: The Earth may have completely frozen and thawed at least five times in its history.

Cycles of freezing and thawing, supercontinents turning into islands are all part of the dynamic nature of the Earth's cracked crust. Driven by heat from deep within the planet, the pieces of the crust rub against each other, slide over one another or pull apart. You can see the same effect on northern lakes during spring thaw. Ice breaks into large slabs that jostle against each other forming cracks, ridges or lines of open water. The motion of the Earth's plates happens slowly over much longer periods but the change is constant. A time traveller visiting the Earth hundreds of millions of years from now will see continents and oceans almost unrecognizable from those we see today.

Most of this plate tectonic action happens in the deepest parts of the oceans, which is why this theory wasn't developed until the 1950s. We simply didn't know what the bottom of the sea looked like. Until the invention of sonar, then submarines capable of diving down through eighteen kilometres of ocean water, the largest cracks in the Earth were completely unknown—which is why Robert Ballard was so excited about seeing it all first hand.

A year or so after that interview in the barn, I tried using Bob Ballard's living Earth analogy on television during one of my regular appearances on "Canada AM." Before going live on air, I went to the studio cafeteria and asked for a semi-soft boiled egg to use as a prop. The chef asked, "What do you mean, semi-soft?"

I said I wanted the yolk liquid but the white of the egg

cooked, so it was only soft in the middle. The chef said she would see what she could do and would deliver it to the studio. It seemed like a good plan.

About a minute before we were to go on air the chef arrived with three eggs on a plate. She said, "This one is two minutes, this one is about three and this one I'm not sure."

Now, the thing that makes live television so exciting is that you only get one chance, there are no retakes, you are without a net before the whole country, so whatever happens, that's what the audience sees. The red light above the camera winks on and the floor director points at the host. We're on.

I begin my explanation of plate tectonics using what I learned from Ballard.

"Scientists understand earthquakes and volcanoes better because they now have a clearer image of how the Earth behaves on the inside. In fact, the Earth is a lot like an egg . . ."

The moment of truth arrives when I must choose which of the three eggs is indeed soft boiled. Even though I have been told the cooking times, I realize I don't have a clue how long it takes to cook a soft-boiled egg. Door number one, door number two . . . I go for the least cooked of the three, figuring I will be guaranteed a liquid centre. Holding the egg in the palm of one hand and a knife in the other, I cheerfully announce to the host, "The inside of the Earth looks something like this . . ." and slice completely through the egg in one quick stroke. The yolk is liquid all right. So is the white, in fact the whole egg looks like it hasn't been cooked at all. The entire liquid contents run through my fingers and onto the plate.

"Actually it's not like that at all," I say, trying not to miss a beat even though my hands are now completely covered with egg. I am faced with another decision. One of the two remaining eggs was cooked a minute longer than the one that has just exploded in my hand. The other is a complete unknown. Time passes quickly when you are on live television and I really want this story to be about the Earth and not about eggs. I go for the unknown, figuring it is most likely to be well done so it will at least hold together and I can get on with the illustration.

"Let's try that again," I continue, taking careful aim with the knife. It's perfect. The egg cleaves neatly in half, revealing a cooked white and yellow yolk just soft enough to still be liquid yet thick enough to remain in the centre and not run out. The camera zooms in for a close-up as I point to the thin shell, then to the semi-solid white and liquid yolk, making comparisons to the structure of the Earth.

"The Earth has a thin crust that covers a white-hot mantle which has a molten iron core in the middle." This was brilliant, I was getting excited. With the handle of the knife I tap the shell lightly to crack it in different places. Next I peel off one of the larger pieces.

"Now the crust of the Earth is cracked like this, and the pieces are called plates," I explain, feeling very confident that my analogy is working well. The piece in my fingers even looks like North America.

"A plate is about the size of North America, and the edges are rough, just like the edge of this piece of shell." I can't believe how well this is working. I then rub the piece of eggshell against a piece still attached to the egg and continue, "Now when the pieces rub against each other, the jagged edges catch, then crumble and crunch which is the basic cause of earthquakes."

This is unbelievable. The camera is getting all the action, the egg looks beautiful in close up, the clock ticks down the final seconds, leaving me just enough time for my grand concluding statement. "The Earth may seem dead to us, but in fact it's alive with activity, it's just like a living . . ." Now the word I intended to use was "organism," but that's not what came out.

To this day I think of Bob Ballard's perspective on the Earth, especially when travelling. It gives new meaning to the term scenery. When I fly west from Calgary to Vancouver, row upon row of the Rocky Mountains look to me like a crumpled rug that has been pushed up against a wall. As North America slowly slides west, moving at about the speed your fingernails grow, it runs into the Pacific plate. The land is squeezed under enormous pressure folding upwards until it cracks into jagged mountain peaks. You can see the folds in the rock while driving along the incredible highway that runs between Banff and Jasper. Mount Rundle, the mountain always featured in the postcard pictures of Banff, clearly shows how land that was once flat has been tilted up on its end. The western slope of the mountain, the side facing the town, is a smooth face that gently curves up to the peak. It's still covered with forest the way it was when it was flat ground. The eastern slope is a steep precipice, a vertical face striped with many layers of multicoloured rock. Those layers were originally layers of mud on the floor of a vast sea that once covered central North America seventy million years ago. The ancient sea floor now stands exposed by the powerful forces of a continent in motion.

The really big cracks in the eggshell crust of the Earth, the edges of the big plates that Robert Ballard explored at the bottom of the ocean, are more difficult to see unless you happen to have a deep-diving submarine at your disposal. But there are a few places where the edges of the plates can be seen on land. Probably the most famous is California's legendary San Andreas fault. Running 1,100 kilometres from Mexico to just north of San Francisco, the fault marks the contact point between North America and the floor of the Pacific Ocean. Along this borderline between continents, the two plates are sliding past one another rather than colliding, which gives Californians the uneasy feeling that the Earth really does move under their feet.

During a recent trip there I saw the famous fault along with a busload of other journalists and geologists. Most California tour guides point out the homes of the stars; we were shown rock formations and rift zones.

The tour begins along a section of the original Route 66, which runs right down the centre of the fault near San Bernadino. Driving down the famous highway with the old tune "Get your kicks on Route 66" running through our heads, we follow along the bottom of a long valley lined with rounded hills on either side. In some places ridges look like they have been sliced with a knife and shifted so the edges don't line up.

The scientists describe how the two sides of the San Andreas fault have moved so much the mountains on either side of the valley look different because they come from two different geological areas. Those on the east side, part of North America, were once hundreds of kilometres north. California, sitting on the Pacific plate, was once much farther south and has moved up to be beside them.

Looking along the valley, I realize it is similar in shape and size to some of the rift valleys Dr. Ballard explored by submarine at the bottom of the ocean. I imagine being crammed with two other people into an eight-foot sphere peering out at a valley like this through tiny portholes into the total darkness of the deep, seeing only what reflects in the beams of the headlamps. It makes me appreciate the comfort of the bus and the California sunshine.

What we really want to see is the actual fault itself, the big crack, the stuff of legends . . . maybe we will even feel it move . . . . . After all, this is the meeting place of two of the largest piece of the Earth's crust, it must be impressive. Well, it was, sort of.

Near the end of the valley we scramble down the steep slope of a small cliff. Turning back towards the face of the cliff Dr. Tom Henyay points to a thin dark line running diagonally across the soil. "Well, there it is, the San Andreas fault."

"That's it?" I think to myself. "You've got to be kidding. This is just a little line in crumbly white powder—where are the huge slabs of rock grinding past one another?"

If the thin line hadn't been pointed out I would have missed it completely. But hey, Americans are proud of their famous features and I don't want to be the one to tell them their big fault is about as impressive as a crack in the sidewalk. Fortunately someone else raised the issue of the apparent "simplicity" of the fault.

With a kind smile Dr. Henyay, a geologist at the University of Southern California, explains that you won't see great slabs of rock grinding past one another anywhere along the fault because millions of years of rubbing has ground the rock into a fine powder that looks like flour. This is rock dust between the two edges of the plates, like sawdust between wood and sandpaper. The flour between the plates extends several kilometres on either side of the fault.

I begin to appreciate the scale of the scene we are standing in. The mountains we have just driven between are actually made of this rock flour which has been squeezed up from within the giant crack. That's one heck of a big piece of sandpaper!

OK, so we don't see huge slabs of rock, but we do see an actual line in the ground. The soil on either side of the fault is different so a distinct straight line between the two runs like a scar across the side of the hill at about a forty-five-degree angle. It could easily be mistaken for a simple line between two different soil types but Dr. Henyay explains that the line continues underground for about six kilometres.

I straddle the line, with one foot on the Pacific plate and one on the North American, wondering what will happen if the fault lets go at that very moment.

Actually, I have a fairly good idea what happens when the San Andreas lets go, thanks to an earthquake simulator at the University of British Columbia. A large movable platform reproduces the motion of the ground during an earthquake. The seismic record from a real earthquake is fed into a computer which then commands powerful hydraulic rams under the platform to move and shake exactly as the ground did during the quake. Scientists use the simulator to test models of buildings for earthquake resistance. When the ground moves during an earthquake it jiggles back and forth with a rhythm that can make buildings sway. If the rhythm continues long enough, and it matches the natural frequency of the building, the swaying becomes larger and larger until the bricks, glass and steel can no longer take it and the building collapses. There are two schools of thought on how to get around that problem: One is to make the building flexible enough so it will bend like wheat in the wind. But if it's too flexible people on the top floors will get seasick every time a storm passes. The other is to design the building with enough strength to hold itself together but the extra materials needed to make it strong add to the construction cost. Most tall buildings in earthquake zones are a compromise between the two.

The three-metre-high steel model sitting on the earthquake

simulator had an experimental but not really practical solution: The whole thing was sitting on ball bearings. I stood on the platform beside the model and prepared for a ride through the most destructive earthquake in North American history, the great San Francisco quake of 1906.

At 5:12 a.m. on April 18, the people of the city were rudely awakened by a terrible rumbling deep in the ground. The San Andreas runs right under that city and it had just let go. The steel platform beneath my feet took me back in time to that dreadful morning.

The quake begins with an almost gentle back-and-forth motion. If you were lying in a bed it would feel like someone was tugging at the frame, barely enough to wake you up. Suddenly the floor sweeps out from under my feet like a loose rug, sliding about two metres to one side. Then just as suddenly it sways back in the opposite direction, repeating the action again and again with such swiftness there is no chance to regain my balance. I grab onto the steel structure of a model building sitting on the platform for support, but it sways violently back and forth as well, offering little relief. During the uneasy ride I try to imagine the terror of being inside a swaying building with the floor moving in these violent jerks, the walls crumbling from the strain. That terrible morning in San Francisco chimneys toppled, church bells clanged wildly as the ground under the entire downtown core rocked like a stormy sea.

For a brief instant the oscillations die down as though the worst is over. But just as I relax my grip a second round of shaking sends me stumbling again. The violent motion of the ground in San Francisco lasted about one minute, but for three full days, the entire city burned to the ground. It was Californians' most deadly lesson in the silent hazard that lay beneath their feet. The 1906 earthquake, a magnitude 7 on the Richter scale, shook an area of 967,000 square kilometres, but actually, the tremor itself was only responsible for part of the damage. Most of the destruction to San Francisco came later when fires broke out and raged uncontrollably through the closely packed wooden buildings. The soft landfill on which most of the city was built shifted during the quake, rupturing the watermains so firefighters could do little more than watch the inferno consume twenty thousand buildings.

The horrible scenes of destruction and death from Turkey or any developing country are the failure of poorly constructed buildings. An earthquake alone would not kill anyone. As I experienced on the quake platform, the motion of the ground might make you fall off your feet but that's about it. As cities grow larger and buildings grow taller, the threat of damage from earthquakes is rising every year. Most countries cannot afford the extra reinforcing required to make buildings earthquake-proof so the collapse of tall structures every time the ground moves is inevitable.

Even when strict building codes are in place, such as in California and all major cities along the West Coast, people find ways around them, as we saw in 1989. A relatively minor tremor set the Marina district of San Francisco ablaze because wooden buildings had been erected on soft landfill. The shifting soil splintered the weak walls, rupturing gas lines which torched the huge woodpile. How easily disasters are forgotten.

We tend to think of the ground as the only firm foundation upon which we feel secure. How do people feel when the very foundation of life itself, the ground on which we stand can no longer be trusted? What does it feel like when there is literally no place to run?

Despite all its fame, the San Andreas fault, which runs outside the city through the sparsely populated mountains, is not the one that causes all the damage in the Los Angeles area of California. The damaging earthquakes come from smaller offshoots of the big fault, which are constantly releasing the strain built up on the San Andreas. The smaller cracks run right under housing developments and city buildings, so any movement there causes a lot of damage. The big one only lets go every 150 years or so, but when it does, things really start to shake.

"The Big One" lurks in capital letters in the minds of most Californians, but when it does come sometime within the next fifty years, it will be tiny compared to the real big one scientists are worried about. Geologists at the Pacific Geosciences Centre in Sydney, B.C., are concerned about an Earth-rattling quake that could affect the entire West Coast of North America, from California to Vancouver. Hidden beneath the deep waters off the coast of British Columbia is a small piece of the Pacific Ocean floor called the Juan de Fuca plate. Small is a relative term here because the fragment is half the size of Saskatchewan, but this "chip" seems to be causing trouble.

As North America moves west it's colliding with the Pacific plate. Since both plates are floating on the hot liquid rock beneath, the Juan de Fuca plate is forced down under North America as we ride up over the top of it, like a conveyor belt at a grocery-store checkout. The flat part of the belt, where you place your groceries, is the Juan de Fuca plate disappearing under the counter, which is the West Coast of North America. The problem is something jammed between the conveyor and the counter. The pieces of crust seem to be stuck and scientists are worried about what's going to happen when they let go.

Dr. Herb Dragert has been using ultrasensitive instruments along with satellites to measure the movement of Vancouver

Island and found that the town of Tofino on the western shore is rising two to three millimetres a year compared to the east side of the island. In other words, the land is bending upwards like a bowed stick. It will only bend so far before it lets go in a super shakeup called a thrust earthquake. The land suddenly lurches up to twenty metres in a magnitude 9 quake that rattles the entire West Coast of the continent, reducing Victoria, Vancouver, Seattle, San Francisco and Los Angeles to rubble.

The magnitude scale by the way is logarithmic, which means each step up increases by a factor of ten, so a magnitude 9 quake is a hundred times greater than the magnitude 7 that leveled San Francisco in 1906. On top of that, the super quake would feel like it was never going to end. Most quakes are over in about thirty seconds or so; the superquake would go on and on for about two minutes. Few buildings could survive that much rattling of the ground. If the destruction on land seems bad, the giant tremor would add insult to injury by triggering tsunamis, giant ocean waves that would wash over the already ruined coastal cities, then spread across the Pacific Ocean, inflicting more damage, to Japan and China.

The devastation from one of these superquakes would be the worst in North American history: critical lifelines would be severed, and hospitals would lie in ruins while millions of people lay buried under collapsed buildings. It sounds like a pretty bleak forecast and of course everyone would like to know when the big one is going to happen. Dr. Dragert says there is geological evidence along the West Coast shorelines that these superquakes happen every five hundred to seven hundred years. The last one was three hundred years ago. I ask him if we are overdue for the next one. He says, "That depends on whether you are an optimist or a pessimist. The average is five hundred years so it could happen soon or we may have to wait." And that's the rub.

Despite a multitude of incredibly sensitive instruments that can detect every little tremor in the ground, earthquake prediction is a very inexact science. It will never be as accurate as weather forecasts because weather happens every day while large earthquakes show up every few hundred years. Weather forecasters have so many storms on record that they can see patterns, the conditions leading up to a tempest that help them predict when the next one is coming and where it will strike. Geologists have very little data on big quakes, both because they happen so infrequently and because the instruments for detecting them have only been available in the last fifty years. That places the geologists in a delicate position. They know that earthquakes are a fact of life on planet Earth and eventually something is going to give. But without a way to predict accurately when and where the next big one will strike, scientists remain cautiously silent.

Their worst fear is crying wolf, forcing the evacuation of major cities, which leads to chaos, looting, traffic accidents. Public panic could be worse than the effect of the earthquake. So people continue to live with the threat, gambling that the big one will not hit their city in their lifetime. That's the strange irony with earthquakes: they are synonymous with disaster, yet the people who worry about them the least are those who live on top of the faults.

Californians are willing to gamble the benefits of warm climate and Hollywood lifestyle against the risk of an occasional shake. Most people win that gamble. In fact, locals love to joke about their unsteady ground. One resident of Los Angeles told me that he's not worried about "The Big One" because when the San Andreas fault lets go, the rest of North America will slide into the Atlantic.

The life-and-death contrast around earthquakes and volcanoes is true for animal and plant life as well. Volcanic soil is very fertile, and in selected places along the bottom of the ocean, the richest oases of life thrive around volcanic vents. One of the biggest surprises that stunned Robert Ballard during one of his deep diving expeditions in the Pacific in 1977 was the discovery of a colony of giant worms, clams and crabs clustered around hot water springs gushing out of the ocean floor. He was actually studying one of the plate boundaries called a spreading centre. That's the opposite of a collision, where two plates are pulling apart and new molten material oozes up from below to fill in the gap. While gliding along in the total dark of the deep ocean, the headlamps of the submarine shone upon a garden of white creatures clustered around rocky chimneys with black smoke pouring out of their tops. The "smokers" were plumes of hot water rising from within the Earth's crust, carrying a rich brew of minerals and chemicals.

"We were expecting to see hot springs, because it was a volcanically active area," Ballard told me as we sat in the barn loft halfway through the bottle of wine. "But we didn't expect to find any animals. Most of the deep ocean is a desert because sunlight doesn't reach the bottom, yet we had stumbled upon this rich oasis teeming with life."

"So what did you do?" I asked, pouring another two glasses of wine.

"Well it was pretty exciting because there we were, seeing a new form of life for the first time but there wasn't a biologist among us. We didn't know what to call the animals but since we were first to see them we called them anything we wanted. I called one of them the Pompeii worm because it lived on the side of the vent and was constantly getting buried by debris falling down on it."

Later that year I visited the laboratories at Woods Hole where the biologists were frantically studying the creatures Ballard had brought up from the deep. You could feel the excitement in the air as they examined the two-metre-long white worms with crimson red tops and clams the size of dinner plates. One scientist held up a glass tube containing a creature that looked to me like a dandelion fluffball and said, "See this, we have no idea what it is. Fantastic."

It turned out that the bizarre animals thriving around the vents have formed their own complex ecosystem, the first ever found to be living totally without the benefit of sunlight. Instead of using photosynthesis, the base of the food chain on land, this system uses chemosynthesis, where bacteria living in the hot water turn hydrogen sulphide, the stuff that produces that rotten-egg smell in high school chemistry labs, into food and energy. The worms, clams and crabs live off the bacteria forming a complete food chain different from the one we use on land. These colonies are so self-sufficient that if all other life on the planet became extinct, they would probably survive on their own, deep within the darkness of the ocean floor. Here is a dramatic case of life thriving at the mouth of a boiling volcanic cauldron.

Since Ballard's discovery many more vent colonies have been found near hot springs all over the world. A whole new science has emerged to determine how they got started in the first place, and what happens if the volcano upon which they depend erupts.

Verena Tunnicliffe, a Canadian biologist in Victoria, has spent more than a decade studying vent colonies off the coast of British Columbia along the edge of that troublesome Juan de Fuca plate. In 1998 she got the chance to see what happens when a colony is wiped out by an erupting volcano.

When the Axial seamount blew its top no one saw it

because the top of the mountain is three kilometres under water. But the event was loud and clear to marine scientists and military people who listen for strange noises beneath the waves.

Dr. Tunnicliffe had studied vent colonies before the eruption, clustered around the summit of the volcano. The scene that faced her when she returned after the volcano had quieted down was total devastation. Part of the mountaintop had collapsed, some of the hotwater vents had been shut off and there was little sign of life.

So how do these colonies get started again, since volcanoes are popping off all the time? She discovered that secret when she came back again, three months later. Sure enough the bacteria were back, tube worms were growing again and new colonies were sprouting out of the old rubble. It appears that the creatures have a larval stage that can drift on the ocean currents until they come across another hot spring. Obviously, these ecosystems are very tough. Some biologists believe these submarine colonies may have been the birthplace of life on Earth.

Even space scientists are interested in the undersea colonies. At a conference in California, a hot debate rose over the possibility that similar vent systems might exist at the bottom of the ocean believed to be under the ice on Europa, a moon of Jupiter. There's a thought. Perhaps our first contact with aliens won't be with Vulcans or Klingons, but with tube worms and clams.

Humans also have a tendency to live around volcanoes. Pompeii and Herculaneum were destroyed by the eruption of Mount Vesuvius, yet new towns were built on top of the old, now huddled around the base of the still-active volcano. Living with volcanoes is a way of life all the way around the Pacific, a gigantic circle of volcanoes and earthquake zones known as the ring of fire. The ring is responsible for the earthquakes in California, Mexico, Columbia, Japan, Alaska and Vancouver. Mount St. Helen's, Mount Rainier, Mount Chichon in Mexico, Mount Pinotubo in the Philippines, Mount Fuji in Japan all punch holes through the line that marks the edge of the enormous Pacific plate. Almost all of the active zones are heavily populated.

It's difficult to describe the power of a volcano. You really have to experience it to believe it. I've been fortunate to get a taste of Pelée's power on two occasions without being destroyed by the goddess of the volcano.

One opportunity comes by accident during my first visit to Costa Rica. The ring of fire runs right through this tiny country which straddles the centre of Central America. In an area smaller than Ontario no less than five active volcanoes tower above the countryside.

Our destination is an out-of-the-way lodge located on a river well off the main highways. The guide book suggested the route but signs on the main roads in Costa Rica are so hard to follow that, once you head down dirt paths, getting lost is almost a given. With the last glow of daylight rapidly fading in the west, we continue to bump along the very rough path until it is blocked by a fast-moving river. There is no lodge in sight. We can see the road continuing on the other side of the torrent but I'm not willing to attempt a river crossing in a car that was clearly meant for smooth pavement. We turn back.

I have remembered passing a sign at a fork in the road which might lead to other accommodation. Of course it is written in Spanish, but the two words "Volcan Arenal" make sense. That's the name of one of the Costa Rican volcanoes. Late at night is not the best time to go sightseeing, but perhaps there is a hotel in that direction. Night is now completely upon us, which combined with our location off the main highway makes the scenery completely black. There is not even a moon hanging in the sky to provide assistance. Just as I'm thinking the situation looks hopeless I notice a strange sight . . . car headlights in the sky!

Maybe I'm getting tired, but no, there, suspended in the blackness are two beams from car headlights pointed upwards, and they are slowly climbing higher. The jerky motion of the beams proves I am not seeing an airplane. There is obviously a hill hidden in the darkness and that car could be heading to a hotel on the other side. Following the fork in the road, we begin a slow steep climb up the boulder-strewn path. The slope provides a considerable challenge for the small car but eventually, after rounding a house-sized rock we come upon a parking lot full of cars. As my headlights swing over the scene, a whole crowd of people, many sitting on the hoods of the cars, shield their eyes and gesture to me to turn my lights off. I figure we have stumbled upon lover's lane. Oh well, it's a place to stop and contemplate our next move.

I kill the engine, plunging us into what seems like total blackness, but as our eyes adjust to the dark, an eerie sight appears in the sky above. A dim red glow hovers in the night. My vision improves and I see streaks of red, like blood flowing down a wounded shoulder. The volcano is erupting.

I am astounded that people are sitting right on the side of an active volcano. Either they are very naive or they know something I don't. The people watching are not tourists so I figure they know more about the safety of the place than I do. Arenal is a cinder cone, a type of volcano that shoots gas and ash out of its mouth instead of lava. But it's still hot stuff. The conical shape of the volcano itself is hidden in the darkness. All we can see is the glowing cauldron at the summit where red-hot rocks and cinders are blowing into the air and cascading down the steep sides of the cone.

It's an awesome sight and an even more awesome sound. At first I don't realize the noise is coming from the summit. It's a kind of huffing sound, like an old steam locomotive puffing uphill, except these huffs are much stronger and deeper, as though the whole mountain is coughing and wheezing. With each gasp the ground trembles slightly from the violence of the gases escaping from the vent. It feels like standing on the flanks of a giant living beast. The Earth breathes.

The next morning (we did find a hotel) the steep-sided pure cone shape of the volcano stood silhouetted against the morning mist. It looked more like a scene out of a Hollywood musical than of a natural formation. A grey plume drifted off the summit like a banner fed by the fires within. This was a new piece of Earth. The sides of the cinder cone were bare; vegetation hadn't had time to grow yet. We returned that day to the same spot on the side of the mountain we had visited the night before to see the action in daylight. The dim red glow was not visible but the huffing sounds were still belching out of the mountain along with automobile-sized boulders that bounded down the sides of the cone, coming to rest in a cloud of dust and steam.

A resort built against the other side of the mountain was under renovation from an earlier eruption that had destroyed several buildings. The resort owners chose to remain in the same location because of the popular hot springs that bubbled out of the side of the volcano. Again, people were happily living on the edge of destruction.

My second experience with an active volcano was entirely different. In Hawaii, it looked like the Earth was bleeding.

The Hawaiian Islands are one of the few places on Earth where tourists can look into the mouth of an erupting volcano. The island of Hawaii is the largest mountain on Earth. Measured from its base on the sea floor to the summit of Mauna Kea it rises 10,203 metres (33,476 feet), more than a kilometre taller than Mount Everest. The puzzling part of the volcanoes here is their position. Most volcanoes are located around the edge of the Pacific along the ring of fire. Why are the largest volcanoes on the planet located almost exactly in the centre of the ring? They shouldn't really be there right in the middle of the Pacific plate.

The answer came from Canadian scientist J. Tuzo Wilson, who was also one of the founders of the whole plate tectonic theory. He was the first to suggest the idea that in selected places around the world, hot material from deep within the planet rises up in a chimney and burns a hole through the crust. Hawaii, he said, is sitting on top of one of these hot spots.

The hot-spot theory says the chimneys of hot magma remain stationary while the crust of the Earth moves over top. The hot-spot acts like a candle under a piece of paper, burning a hole, but if the paper moves a line of holes will appear with the candle flame poking through the one at the end. If you look at a map of the Pacific Ocean you can see how the "Big Island," Hawaii, is at the southern end of a long chain of extinct volcanoes. Geologists have found that the islands to the north are several million years older than those in the south, and the Big Island is the only one where volcanoes are still erupting today.

The material that fuels the Hawaiian volcanoes is almost pure molten rock with very little gas content compared to

Arenal in Costa Rica. Hawaiian eruptions ooze lava like dripping candle wax rather than bursting explosively. Drive
around the island and you can see broad black trails of lava
that have flowed down the hillsides, sometimes right through
housing developments. But few people are hurt by the creeping lava. It moves so slowly you can literally just step out of
the way and watch it pass like a huge molten worm. At Volcanoes National Park, railings are installed along the edge of
Halemaumau, the steaming lava lake that is the very throat of
the Kilauea volcano.

The most spectacular sight I've seen is where the lava
meets the sea. When lava meets air it cools quickly forming
a crust. Fresh liquid lava continually bubbles out of the volcano and flows through long underground tubes the size of
subway tunnels. At the seashore, these tunnels emerge from
the face of a cliff spewing straight out in a blood-red stream
of liquid rock. The six-hundred-degree lava pours directly
into the blue water of the Pacific, boiling the sea instantly
and raising a white plume of steam that billows thousands of
feet into the blue sky. And you can watch all of this from a
few metres away.

The road around the Big Island has been crossed by a
recent lava flow creating the ultimate dead end. It looks like
someone spilled a large container of liquid tar across the road.
Hawaiian lava moves so slowly it keeps its liquid shape as it
hardens, making it look like it's still in motion. The smooth
surface makes for easy hiking across the lava field to the edge
of the flow. I was there along with a cameraman to shoot the
scene for television so we were lugging a tripod and other
gear over our shoulders.

The scene at the water's edge was like a page out of Dante's
Inferno. Earth, sea and air boil together in a maelstrom of
activity. The huge Hawaiian surf washes up against the cliff

face with a slow, steady rhythm. Each ebb of the waves exposes the stream of lava shooting straight out of the rock in a continuous flow, arching smoothly down to the foamy surf. The jet of molten rock stands unwavering, driven by powerful pressure from within the mountain. In seconds a wave rises and consumes the lava, hissing and boiling, sometimes bursting with steam explosions. The Earth tries to move into the sea; the sea fights back. Within the foamy surf, rocks only seconds old float like sponges, buoyed up by bubbles of steam hissing off their hot surfaces. Above it all, a billowing white cloud rises straight out of the water ascending 3,000 metres (10,000 feet) into the blue sky.

The setting Sun added another dimension to the eerie scene. As the light from the sky turned from blue to indigo, the deep red glow of the lava began to illuminate the steam cloud from within. There was clearly energy below.

Unfortunately, our desire to get that sunset shot kept us out on the lava field too long to get back to the car before dark. The Sun sets quickly in the tropics. It was a delicate walk back across the uneven ground trying to follow the feeble beam of Rick's single penlight flashlight.

Less than halfway back the batteries die and we stop to get our bearings. Once again my eyes adjust to the dark, and once again I see blood-red streaks coming down the sides of the volcano. Windows in the lava tubes, or cracks in the ground where the glow from subterranean rivers of lava shines through stretch up the slope for five or six kilometres. The whole side of the mountain is lit up. I try to imagine the huge chamber of molten magma lurking six kilometres beneath the mountain, the source of this glowing ember. It's hard to fathom energy on that scale.

It's in situations like that, where I'm struck with a sense of the dynamic nature of our planet, that I think back to that day in Cape Cod sitting in Robert Ballard's barn discussing the living Earth. Thanks to his perspectives on the planet I can more deeply appreciate straddling the San Andreas fault or staring into the mouth of a volcano.

At one point in our conversation I asked him how, as a person who's studied the Earth literally from top to bottom, he sees our planet. He replied:

"You know, three-quarters of the surface of the Earth is in total darkness, covered by the oceans. I've been to the bottom of the ocean more often and in more places than anyone else. And while it's very interesting, I wouldn't want to live there. It's cold, it's dark, it's mostly desert. When you look at the little bit that's sticking above the water, large areas are frozen, large areas are deserts and after you take all that away there isn't a hell of a lot left that we can live on. So it really makes me appreciate the few acres I have here on Cape Cod."

We raised another toast to his new barn.

(About ten years after I did that interview, Robert Ballard entered the history books when he used the deep-diving submarine to discover the wreck of the *Titanic*.)

TORNADOES AND TOILET BOWLS

Getting the dirt on vortices from
Arizona to Australia

STREaks of sand blow across the road like drifting snow. Searing crosswinds blast my face like a huge blow-dryer aimed at my head. The motorcycle leans into the wind while the distant horizon fades behind an orange haze of blowing dust. I think about turning back but the scene in the rear-view mirror shows the same fury. I continue on while a merciless Sun bakes my bare forearms. Midsummer on the Arizona desert is a place for mad dogs and Canadian tourists, but no place for a lone motorcyclist.

Most of my early exploration of North America has been alone on two wheels. It's a magnificent way to see and feel the land. Freed from the confines of windows and roof, the continuous outdoor experience of a bike is like taking a huge walk across the country. The fragrance of fresh blossoms, the metallic taste of pollution, the chill of high altitude and the heat of lowlands all wash over your body, adding a dimension to travel unknown to people inside metal capsules. Of course the elements can also provide less enjoyable riding experiences. No matter what route you follow, rain, lightning, hail, even snow are likely to catch up sooner or later. Long-distance riders get first-hand experience wearing the weather:

raindrops pelt the face like bullets then find their way through rain suits into places you'd really like to keep dry. Fingers freeze around the handlebars while a deep cold seeps into the core of your body producing uncontrollable shakes that can only be calmed by a hot bath . . . ah yes, the joys of motorcycling.

An experienced rider learns to read the sky and tries to avoid these atmospheric assaults before they inflict their wrath. Storm clouds have a particular shape and colour that tells of their direction and severity. A sudden change in temperature is a warning that you have crossed the line into territory where two air masses are about to do battle. If a weather system does hit a rider there are two choices: stop and take shelter, or continue on with the risk of getting cold and wet. Too often I have taken the cold and wet route for the sake of covering more ground in less time—after all I'm a Canadian, we're used to the cold, right?

Well, I may have experienced cold but I was not prepared for the power of heat when I made a foolish attempt to cross the Arizona desert on a blistering July afternoon.

I was on my way to the Grand Canyon and had stopped at Mesa Verde, where the ancient Anasazi people built elaborate stone structures on a cliff face near the top of a large, flat-topped mountain called a mesa. Nestled like a bee's nest under a huge rock overhang, the stone buildings look out over a magnificent view of the surrounding territory. This was my last sightseeing spot at high altitude. I had spent several days in the cool air of the mountains and this was the point where I would head down for my first desert experience.

The temperature seemed to rise at every hairpin turn of the road coming down from the mesa. In the less than fifteen minutes it took to descend, my leather jacket became too hot to wear. I was anxious to cover some ground and figured there was enough daylight remaining to cover the few hundred kilometres to the next town. According to the map it was virtually a straight line across the desert pan; traffic was light, so it should have been a piece of cake. It would have been a simple ride early in the morning or late evening, but what I didn't know is that deserts generate their own kind of nasty weather on sunny afternoons.

An hour into the ride, conditions deteriorate as the afternoon winds whip up the desert dust into a choking veil of orange haze. I push on hoping the full fury of the dust storm will hold off long enough for me to make it through to the next town. There is nowhere to stop anyway; the flat, treeless landscape offers no shelter of any kind. I have foolishly underestimated the intensity of the midday desert environment.

At the point where I begin to question my decision to continue, the engine sputters and the speedometer needle slowly sinks towards zero. The motorcycle seems to have more sense than I do. It wants to stop. Suddenly the reality of my precarious predicament hits me like the hot wind. Images from every western movie I've seen flash through my mind. There I am, sun-baked, crawling across the sand like a half-crazed cowboy gasping, "Water . . . water." OK, it probably wouldn't come to that but the desert environment is becoming more hostile by the minute and I realize how silly I am to be out there without protection.

As I watch the speedometer needle continue its steady drop I consider my options: die, or abandon the bike on the side of the road and hope for a ride into the next town. Option number one is not very attractive, but neither is option number two because most of what I own is strapped to the back of the bike. (I didn't own much in those days.) But the bike doesn't seem to care about its cargo; it's determined to cease its forward motion.

As the blowing dust begins to close down all visibility, a solitary gas station appears like a ghostly apparition out of the red haze. The engine quits but I'm still coasting just fast enough to roll off the road, under a rusty sign squeaking back and forth in the wind, finally coming to rest under a canopy over the gas pumps. At least it provides some shelter from the Sun. No one comes out of the building.

Inside the combination gas station, grocery store, post office, mail-order desk and snack bar, a few older men sit quietly around a counter drinking coffee. It's one of those places where clocks seem to run a little slower and patience is the first tool used to solve problems.

My entrance is classic John Wayne-western style. The door squeaks open and all eyes turn to the dusty stranger in leather pants filling the entrance. All I need is a six-shooter strapped to my thigh to complete the scene. Nobody speaks.

"Do you have a mechanic who knows something about motorcycles?" I inquire.

The men look at each other, shrug their shoulders then look back at me with their heads slowly shaking in silence.

"Is there anyone around here who does?"

A few more seconds pass before the one behind the counter replies, "You have to go about two hours that way," pointing towards the large cloud of red dust growing thicker on the horizon. Obviously I'm not going anywhere for a while.

I thank him for the information, order a cold drink, and take it back outside where I face the task of poking and prodding the engine of my motorcycle for a clue to its reluctance. Meanwhile the howl of the wind intensifies to a roar. A garbage can blows over with a hollow clang; pieces of paper, plastic containers and anything else not tied down take flight along with an endless blast of gritty sand beating against my sweaty skin.

A sudden gust pushes me off-balance. I cling to the motor-cycle as the whistling wind roars loudly, whipping my hair so hard it hurts my scalp. Looking up I see an unbelievable scene—the air seems to come alive. The entire desert view is filled with a swirling red cloud of dirt. A dust devil, little brother of the Texas Twister, cousin of the tornado, is heading straight towards me.

The red column of churning dust stands at least ten storeys high. It seems to be walking along the ground stirring up the sand, kicking debris and rocks the size of my fist around at a dizzying pace. I brace myself against the motorcycle as the devil passes closely behind the garage, roaring like a jet engine, then ambles slowly across the road I have just been driving on. The base of the funnel covers the entire width of the highway. Had my engine not quit I probably would have become part of that flying debris. The slithering vertical tube sways its mid-section like an erotic dancer as it meanders unimpeded across the desert pan. It seems to have a life of its own, a crimson giant taking a leisurely stroll across the land, oblivious to anything in its path and destructive to anything unfortunate enough to be in its way.

I had heard about dust devils, usually referred to as the harm-less little relative of the tornado. But what I saw that after-noon on the desert was not little and it was a very powerful demonstration of one of nature's most destructive forms, the vortex.

Dust devils, tornadoes, hurricanes, the little funnel that forms over your bathtub drain are all vortices. They are one of the most common forms in nature, found in all moving liquids and gases. The shape is always the same but the size can range from tiny eddies behind rocks in a babbling brook to a thousand-kilometre-wide tropical storm. It's not hard to make a vortex, which is why they are so common. All you need is a moving fluid, either liquid or gas, that you suddenly force into a new direction and speed.

Pull the plug in a sink and a vortex usually forms over the drain where the water, flowing slowly along the bottom of the sink, suddenly speeds up and drops down the hole. Two speeds, two directions converging at one place, that's a setup for a vortex. The water in a sink does this naturally because it's the most efficient way the water can pass through the drain. The hole in the centre of the funnel allows air in the pipe to escape upwards while the water moves downwards.

This ability of vortices to move fluids quickly can be very useful. Toilet bowls are designed to make sure a vortex forms so the bowl empties as quickly as possible. If the water had to go straight down, the air in the drainpipe would bubble up through the, uh, contents of the bowl causing the toilet to glug glug glug. Imagine how unpleasant that would be!

The basic principles behind vortices are always the same, regardless of the size or location. Fluids moving in different directions interact with each other and swing around in a circular dance. Fast-moving water in a river and slower water behind a rock produce little whirlpools where they meet. Large masses of warm and cold air over the tropical oceans run into each other and twist into the spiral shape of hurricanes. Even in deep space vortices are found churning among the clouds of the giant planets Jupiter, Saturn, Uranus and Neptune, even in the hot gases spiralling around a black hole. It's a form nature uses again and again to transport energy from one place to another.

The dust-devil vortex I encountered in Arizona was created by currents of air moving in two different directions, sideways and upwards. On summer afternoons the Sun heats desert sand like a frying pan, sending plumes of hot air high into the sky. Cooler air from distant mountains passes over the desert and runs into the rising hot air. The upward-moving air is twisted into a spiral motion by the cooler air rolling past it. It's the same effect as water going down a drain, just turned upside down. The dust devil is formed by air spiralling upwards rather than water going down.

There is a common misconception that water going down a drain spins because of the Coriolis effect, the turning of the Earth. That's not it. The spin is determined by the shape of the sink; and the motion of the water before you pull the plug. Water seldom sits still in a sink, your hands stir it up or the faucet was a little off-centre when you turned it on setting up a swirling motion in the beginning. You can easily make the vortex spin either way by stirring the water with your finger before pulling the plug. Another myth says water spins down drains in the opposite direction south of the equator. It doesn't. I tried it when visiting Australia and got the same results: I could make it spin either way. Toilet bowls spin the water in whatever direction the nozzles under the rim are pointed. In the small survey I've conducted, toilets seem to all spin their vortices in a counterclockwise direction. I don't know if toilet bowls in Australia are designed to aim the other way.

Dust devils also spin in either direction because like a sink full of water, they are too small to be affected by the turning Earth. If the Coriolis effect made small things spin it would be difficult to walk in a straight line down the street, baseballs would always turn to the right and we would all get headaches from the fluids swirling around in our brains. The spin of a small vortex depends on the conditions when the two fluids meet.

Imagine standing alone on ice skates minding your own

business when a friend comes careening towards you out of control. The best way to avoid getting hurt is to grab onto each other just before the collision and spin around on the spot. The energy of forward motion is turned into a quick rotation. You could spin in either direction depending on the angle your friend approaches. If you pull your friend closer, the spinning motion will speed up, according to the principles of angular momentum. Anything that spins carries energy in its motion. If the circle of the spin gets smaller the same amount of energy is concentrated into a shorter circle, so the spin becomes faster. Figure skaters take advantage of this same principle to increase their spins by drawing their arms in close to the body. That is also what keeps vortices going.

In a vortex, the air or water is drawn out of the centre by the spinning action. This creates low pressure which draws the outside air in closer, increasing the speed, producing even lower pressure, drawing the circle in tighter and so on. Eventually a balance is reached where the outward force of the spin balances the suction inwards towards the hole in the centre. You can see this in the bathtub drain as the water spins so quickly a hole forms in the centre. The water around the hole is trying to fall inwards but it's held out by its spin, the same force that keeps people in their seats on spinning amusement rides. So the water follows a spiral path down the drain. This balancing of all the forces makes vortices extremely stable. As long as energy is available the vortex will maintain its shape.

My dust devil was powered by the energy of the Sun as heat rises off the desert sand. The low-pressure centre of my Arizona dust devil was strong enough to pull in an amazing amount of dirt and debris that it vacuumed up off the desert floor. I was thankful that my arms and legs were not part of that material; it certainly had the power to toss me and my motorcycle a considerable distance.

Despite their power, especially when viewed from close up, dust devils seldom do much damage. There are no trees to uproot on the desert and the few scattered buildings are strong enough to withstand their fury. But had I been travelling farther east in Kansas or Texas my encounter with a vortex could have been deadly serious.

"Tornado Alley," running right up the centre of North America from the Gulf of Mexico to southern Ontario, gets hit by more tornadoes than any other place in the world, more than three hundred a year. Although the scale is much larger, the same principles of colliding air masses that produce dust devils also generate their larger relatives. Warm moist air travelling up from the Gulf of Mexico meets cool dry air sweeping down from the mountains. The meeting place is over the flat landscape of the plains. Tornadoes themselves don't stand alone like dust devils; they are part of larger rotating thunderstorms.

Big storm systems are large enough to be affected by the Coriolis force and they do turn in the opposite direction south of the equator. In the Northern Hemisphere, the turning of the Earth rotates the storms in a counterclockwise direction.

Exactly how tornadoes form is still not well understood because they happen in such violent circumstances that it's difficult to observe them without getting killed. Even the tornado chasers who were glorified in the movie *Twister* have had little luck catching one in action. Their Totable Tornado Observatory, "TOTO" (intentionally named after Dorothy's dog in *The Wizard of Oz*), was designed to be swept up into a funnel where its instruments would record wind speeds and pressure. The problem is getting TOTO into the funnel without killing the scientists. The 180-kilogram, barrel-shaped device has been carted around in the back of a pickup and dropped in what is believed to be the path of a tornado while the scientists dash for safety. But as proof of the unpredictability of tornadoes, TOTO has never seen the inside of a tornado vortex.

Newer instruments, especially Doppler radar, are able to monitor the motions of water drops in a storm from a safe distance. A new image of tornado formation is emerging that shows how high-altitude cool winds speeding across the top of a thunderstorm trip over the slower-moving air below. The cool air curls downwards creating a sideways vortex that rolls within the storm like a big log. Hot, moist air rising swiftly upwards through the centre of the storm turns the log on its end, sending a thin funnel downwards from the bottom of the cloud. When the tip of the vortex touches the ground it becomes a tornado, the most powerful storm in nature. Winds up to 450 km/h shatter buildings and whip up dirt and debris into a black shroud that gives tornadoes their ominous appearance.

Stories abound on the destructive power of tornadoes and their peculiar ability to be selective. Neighbouring houses have been completely swept away while those across the street remain untouched. Whole sections of houses have been ripped off their foundations while dishes in cabinets remain unbroken. In 1985 a tornado ripped through southern Ontario passing over the town of Barrie. The destruction to homes was typical for a tornado—roofs missing, frame houses reduced to splinters, large buildings ripped open as though they had exploded.

Following that storm I took a drive through the area trying to see the track of the tornado. The countryside surrounding the city revealed a different kind of damage. Pieces of tin roofing blown off barns were wrapped around tree trunks and telephone poles like tin foil. Forests were cut by occasional clearings that looked like a very large bulldozer had pushed its way through the woods cutting a new road. Trees of all sizes were uprooted by the brute force, pushed over into tangled masses of roots, branches and soil. But the clearings were roads to nowhere. A few hundred metres into the woods the trail of destruction ended in a line of topless trees, their upper halves snapped off as through the great bulldozer had taken to the sky.

This type of spot destruction was once thought to be due to the narrow bottom of a tornado which can hop across the ground pogo-stick style wreaking havoc wherever it touches down. But now a new picture has emerged showing that the inside of a tornado funnel is more complicated than a simple whirling tube. Smaller funnels called suction vortices swirl around inside the main funnel like dancers on a circular stage. Lasting only a few seconds, they possess the highest winds and do most of the damage to buildings. They also explain curious circular streaks resembling scrub brush marks that are often left in fields after a tornado has passed. How three or four smaller funnels can form inside one bigger one is still a problem for the tornado specialists to figure out.

Tornadoes may be nature's most powerful storms but they are not the most destructive. That title goes to hurricanes and typhoons. Twisters only last a matter of minutes, inflicting severe damage in a relatively small area. Hurricanes rage for days and cover thousands of square kilometres, inflicting damage by wind, rain and floods. Yet in structure, hurricanes are still vortices and operate on the same principles as dust devils and drainpipes.

During a visit to the Goddard Space Flight Center in Maryland I saw the action of the largest vortices on the planet. Satellite images of hurricanes are assembled by computers into time-lapse, three-dimensional movies. Using special polarized glasses I was able to look down into the eye of Hurricane

Andrew, which struck Florida in 1992. Born in the warm tropical waters off the coast of Africa, hurricanes start out as clus-
ters of thunderstorms that merge together into a rotating mass
which gains strength as they track across the Atlantic towards
the Caribbean. Their counterparts in the South Pacific, typhoons, spin clockwise towards Southeast Asia and Japan. If
trade winds blowing steadily across the ocean run into high jet
streams moving in a different direction, a vortex begins to
form, this time on a scale covering thousands of kilometres.
Although the storm takes longer to develop, the principle is
still the same: A low-pressure area develops in the centre, the
outer arms of the storm are drawn in, which speeds up the circular motion. Heat from the warm ocean water provides the
energy to keep the system rolling, and when the wind speed
exceeds 120 km/h, the storm is classified as a hurricane.

The three-dimensional computer image of the storm looked
like the angel cakes my mother made when I was a kid, the
kind with a hole in the centre. It also looked exactly like water
going down a drain. But when the image was set in motion, I
could see how much more complicated the action of a hurricane is. Andrew was made up of two enormous vortices spinning in opposite directions, one on top of the other. It looked
as though two storms had been superimposed on the same
image. The lower part of the storm spun counterclockwise,
like all northern hurricanes, but another stream of clouds rose
out of the eye and spiralled in the opposite direction over the
top of the entire storm.

Thanks to the new satellite images, scientists could see how
the eye of the hurricane, normally an area of calm, had its own
violent side. Like the tornado funnel, which carries smaller,
suction vortices within it, the eye of the hurricane spawns
smaller "spun-up" vortices capable of inflicting tremendous
damage in a small area. Air currents called super updrafts rise

out of the eye of the hurricane like smoke from a steaming locomotive. The updrafts cling to the side of the eye wall, where they are twisted as they rise by the turning action of the storm. The twist is spun up further by cloud layers rolling past one another at different speeds. Andrew passed directly over south Florida and Louisiana, making it one of the most destructive storms of the century, causing $30 billion worth of damage

Television news footage usually shows palm trees bent sideways by strong winds and roofs tearing off buildings but most hurricane damage comes from water rather than wind. The low-pressure eye in the centre of the storm, like the centre of a tornado, acts like a vacuum-cleaner hose sucking material up from the ground. But since hurricanes form over water, the ocean itself is picked up in a large dome-shaped bulge that rises under the eye of the storm. The dome may only be a few metres high, but spread over 450 square kilometres, that's a lot of water. The storm moves forward carrying the dome of water with it until it reaches land. When the leading edge of the dome runs into shallow water it slows down, forcing the rest of the dome to pile up behind, forming a wall of water five metres above the normal sea level. If the dome arrives during high tide, and is covered by large waves, the result is a storm surge which crashes over sea walls and sandbags. Poorly constructed buildings in coastal communities, especially in developing countries, are often washed away along with hundreds of lives.

While they are feared by humans, swirling storms are part of every planet that has an atmosphere. Dust devils have been spotted roaming across the deserts of Mars and the largest vortex of all, the great red spot of Jupiter, has been raging for as long as we've had telescopes to see it, more than 350 years. That storm is so large that three entire Earths could be lined up side by side within it.

On a human scale the vortices that twist their way through the Earth's atmosphere are destructive menaces. Scientists talk about fighting the storms, seeding them with ice crystals that trigger rainfall so the storms give up their energy early in a relatively gentle way rather than violently all at once later on. But from the point of view of the Earth's climate, tornadoes and hurricanes are important players that maintain the heat balance of the planet. Vortices are the movers and shakers of the air, transporting energy from one place to another. Dust devils like the one I met in Arizona act as chimneys, where heat from the desert floor is piped up to high altitudes and then is dispersed on the upper winds.

(As I write this section, a severe thunder and hailstorm is raging outside my window. A report just came over the radio that a tornado was spotted about fifty kilometres from here.)

Hurricanes are atmospheric stir sticks that mix the warm air from the tropics with the cold air from the poles. Without the blending effect of storms, too much heat would build up around the middle of the planet and not enough would reach the high latitudes. With ultrahot tropics and ultracold polar regions, the Earth's climate would be very different and probably quite inhospitable without storms to mix it up.

That ability to move energy also makes vortices a nuisance for our speedy technology that moves through air or water. Vehicles are slowed down by unwanted vortices in the air that spin off unaerodynamic parts of the body taking some of the vehicles' energy with them. When I ride my motorcycle down the highway (when it runs), I feel a side-to-side buffeting from the air coming around the windshield. What I'm really feeling are little whirlpools formed when the fast-moving air whipping around the front of the windscreen meets the slower-moving air behind it. The vortices then spin off and hit me on the side of the head. They also lower my gas mileage.

Aircraft designers work very hard to avoid that effect by making airplane bodies as smooth as possible. But even a smooth shape can create whirlpools of air. Watch closely the next time you see a space shuttle landing. The moment it touches down on the runway, smoke from the tires gets caught up in two huge whirlpools on either side of the shuttle just off the wingtips. These are wingtip vortices that are constantly streaming off the wings of high-speed aircraft. Slower-moving air under the wing leaks around the tip and meets faster-moving air moving over the top. The vortices that result can be so powerful on large jumbo jets that small planes following behind can be completely flipped over. That's why small planes often wait a few minutes at the end of a runway when a jumbo takes off ahead of them. They are waiting for the wingtip vortices from the big plane to disperse.

Modern airliners have adopted winglets sticking straight up on the tips of the wings to prevent the vortices from forming and recapture some of that lost energy.

Geese, cormorants and other migrating birds that fly in a V-formation have been taking advantage of wingtip vortices for millennia. The whirlpools coming off the tips of the lead bird provide a little extra lift for the bird following behind. The second bird catches the upward-moving side of the vortex under its wing, saving itself a little energy. It then passes its own wingtip vortices on to the bird behind and so on down the line. This energy-saving travel tip means the lead bird is working harder than the rest which is why the lead changes often during flight.

Any good idea in nature is always spread as far as possible and the use of vortices to improve forward motion has also been found in water. In fact it was the source of a great mystery in marine science: how do whales, dolphins and fish swim so fast?

Dolphins have bodies about the same size as a human and are capable of cruising through the water at about 25 km/h. A human can swim about 2 km/h with the help of fins. Of course you can argue that we don't have a smooth body shape that cuts through the water easily, but even when we design ships and submarines to be as slippery as possible, they still require huge amounts of horsepower relative to their size to move through the water with any speed. A dolphin on the other hand gallops through the seas with a simple wave of its tail.

The great swimming ability of dolphins fascinated biologist Sir James Gray, who first attempted to figure out the secret of their speed in 1936. He did a calculation based on the shape and body size of a dolphin, and how much resistance it would experience moving through the water at full speed. He also calculated how much power is produced by all the swimming muscles in a dolphin's body. He found that the amount of horsepower needed to move a dolphin at top speed was seven times more than its muscles were capable of producing. The dolphin shouldn't be able to swim as fast as it does. Obviously, the dolphins knew something the scientists didn't. This became known as Gray's Paradox and stood for years as one of the great unsolved mysteries of marine science.

I've had the opportunity to see the amazing speed of dolphins in the wild on several occasions. The first was on a cruise ship off the coast of Mexico. An excited passenger came running down the deck shouting, "Dolphins on the right of the ship." (Clearly this person wasn't a sailor or he would have said starboard side.) Everyone rushed to the railings, and there, extending all the way to the horizon was the largest pod of Pacific silver-sided dolphins I've ever seen. The surface of the water churned from the wake of thousands of animals all swimming at tremendous speed on a course intersecting our own. The ship was cruising at eighteen knots on a course that cut right through the centre of the pod. Our presence didn't disturb the animals in the least. They simply parted to allow us to pass through as though we were nothing more than another very large member of the group. Many took advantage of the ship's wake, leaping and surfing among the permanent rollers that followed us. Looking down from above we could easily see the entire shape of the animals, mostly black with a silver streak running down the side as though it had been sprayed on. Many swam in pairs, moving in perfect synchrony like greyhounds of the sea, their bodies pumping up and down, taking several strokes just beneath the surface then a smooth leap in the air. Stroke, stroke, leap, stroke, stroke, leap, half-swimming, half-flying. Any dolphin acts I've seen in public aquariums are lame compared to these wild ocean thoroughbreds racing across the surface of the sea.

It was exactly this astounding ability to speed through the water up to 25 km/h that fascinated Gray. Later studies showed that most fish share this secret. If you have ever tried to keep up with a fish while swimming you know what I mean. A small silvery animal about the size of my hand provided a quick lesson in swift swimming while I was snorkelling on a reef in the Bahamas. It was swimming along just below the surface with a sort of sideways motion that enabled it to keep an eye on me while keeping a constant distance in front of my mask. Perhaps it was curiosity, or maybe it was used to being fed by people, but it had an amazing ability to keep itself just out of reach no matter how fast or slowly

I swam. When I stopped it stopped, the faster I swam, the quicker it moved, matching my motion turn for turn, always keeping the same distance ahead like a small shuttle craft caught in the tractor beam of a starship. I used to think of myself as a fairly strong swimmer until this little fish taught me a lesson. When I began furiously kicking my fins and clawing the water with my arms in what I thought was a burst of speed, the animal effortlessly held its distance for a few seconds as if to say "Is that the best you can do?" then shot off like it had warp drive. My mouth actually dropped open with the surprise and I nearly choked on a gulp of water, feeling like the hapless Coyote left in the dust by the fleeting Roadrunner.

The paradox of fast fish and dashing dolphins remained unsolved until 1993 when a group of engineers at the Massachusetts Institute of Technology tried to build a mechanical fish. Whenever science tries to imitate nature it often overlooks something important. The "Tuna-sub" looked like a fish and it was supposed to swim like a fish with motors, gears and pulleys to flap the tail, but no matter how furiously the fake fin flapped, the machine couldn't match the performance of its marine counterparts. Realizing there had to be more to this problem than sheer muscle power, the researchers did the obvious: they went back to watching fish swim around in an aquarium.

After a great deal of fish gazing, and probably a lot of human gazing on the part of the fish, the scientists came up with the solution which had been hiding in the water itself . . . vortices. It turns out that as a fish swims along, its movement through the water sets up small whirlpools that roll along the side of its body. The sideways motion of the fish's head when it swims, back and forth as though it's always saying no, generates whirlpools alternately on one side of the body then the other. These little vortices remain intact as they flow down the side of the fish, cradled in the S-shape its body makes as it swims forward. The rolling vortices act as little roller bearings, reducing the friction between the fish's skin and the water. But that only explained part of the paradox. The real kicker comes when the vortices reach the end of the body.

By the time they reach the tail, the fish gives a little flick which throws the little whirlpools off the tip of the tail, providing a little boost. The action of throwing these masses of swirling water backwards produces an opposite reaction moving the fish forward. It's the same principle used by rockets . . . throw something in one direction, you go the other. The fish gets back energy it spent creating the vortices in the first place. The bundles of water act like coiled springs storing energy until they are released by the tail. Dolphins, porpoises and whales do the same thing with an up-and-down motion of the body and tail.

The engineers redesigned their mechanical fish, adding joints to the body so it could simulate the snake-like motion of a swimming fish, and sure enough the paradox was almost solved. Dr. Michael S. Triantafyllou, head of the project, says there is still a little energy unaccounted for, but based on what is now known, flapping fins could one day replace propellers on ships. A fin mounted sideways across the stern of the boat, like the flat tail of a whale, would deliver more thrust with less motion than a propeller. The fin covers a much larger area so it would move more water with each flap. This would be particularly useful for flat-bottomed cargo ships that need to enter shallow waters because the fin would not need to extend much below the waterline. The one minor stumbling block the engineers need to work out is eliminating the counter-motion of the rest of the ship which would tend to bob up and down as well. Passengers on cruise ships would have trouble holding onto their drinks if the hull was nodding

up and down like the body of a dolphin. Walking down a hallway would be quite a stagger even without the drink if the
ship was swaying side to side like a fish.

Fish fins, airplane wings, hurricanes, tornadoes, dust devils
and drainpipes: that's quite a wide range for one natural
phenomenon. Vortices are like spirits, mostly invisible, ever-
present, usually friendly, sometimes menacing. They are the
babble of a babbling brook, the flap in a flag, the animation of
air. Look around on a windy day and you'll see them, perhaps
they will brush your face as they curl around the corner of a
building. You might catch them on a fall day frolicking like
children, tossing leaves into the air in a circular dance. On a
small scale they seem almost playful, but if you ever have a
close encounter with even a medium-sized vortex, it's an
experience you will never forget. The dust devil passing by
me that hot afternoon in Arizona was an awesome demonstration of nature's power.

As I watched it stroll across the sand, the roar fading into
the distance, I realized how lucky I was that my engine had
decided to quit at exactly the right time. My journey across
the country could have come to an untimely end.

Was it the spirit of the vortex that spared my life?

Not quite.

The bike had run out of gas.

It wouldn't be the first time I found myself out on the edge
of survival with a shortage of vital fluids.

PAIN AND PANACEAS

*Tips for a tropical jaunt or
a trip to the dentist*

A COCONUT CLINGS TO ITS treetop roost by a few reluctant strands that my knife is unable to slash. I'm ten metres above the ground near the top of a coconut tree trying to get a meal. During the next few minutes I will experience the most intense pain in my life and witness my brain's amazing ability to control that pain for the sake of survival.

I got myself alone up a tree by trying to play Robinson Crusoe on a sparsely populated island in the Philippines. It was part of a solo adventure around the world that brought me to some of the smaller outer islands that make up this Pacific archipelago. We all dream of being alone on a deserted beach and this was a perfect place to find one. I had my backpack, my tent, some food, I wanted to be alone. How was I to know that this adventure would turn into an exercise in discomfort and pain management as I struggled to get myself back to civilization.

The main form of transportation among the small islands is by outrigger canoe operated by local fishermen. Long and narrow with outrigger pontoons on both sides, the vessels are painted with traditional bright patterns from the days when they were powered by six or eight men with paddles. Now small gas engines do the paddling and solo captains fill the boats with tourists. I asked one of the agreeable young men to take me to a beach where there were no people. "Why do you want to do that?" he inquired.

"Because I want to be alone."

He didn't get it, but took me to exactly the place I had in mind, a long stretch of white sand lined with swaying palms, caressed by rolling surf from an aquamarine sea . . . and not a person or building in sight. It was perfect. As I jumped over the bow of the canoe the driver asked, "When would you like to come back?"

"Don't bother," I said, "I'll get back on my own."

He left with a very puzzled look on his face. Crazy tourists.

It probably was crazy considering I'm a city boy at heart, no one knew where I was and I had no radio or cell phone, but the island was big enough that I knew I could find people if necessary. The first hours were spent running up and down the sand, diving into the surf, snorkelling on the reef, lying in the shade of the palm trees, all those activities we dream about back home sitting in winter rush-hour traffic. The Sun painted the clouds with flaming pastels as it settled into the ocean while I settled into the comfort of a small campfire, a perfect ending to day one, just like in the travel brochures. That was also the end to my comfort.

There's a reason people don't sleep much on beaches . . . bugs. I was eaten alive all night by red ants and other creepy crawlies that feasted on my flesh. It's astounding how those little insect needles can cause so much discomfort.

Pain is one of those necessary evils in life. We need it to know that something is wrong with the body, yet we do everything possible to avoid it. A tiny pinprick or insect bite can seem excruciating, while severe wounds from car accidents or war often produce almost no pain at all. Filters in the nervous system can stop pain signals from getting to the brain, a process that has fascinated doctors, psychiatrists and philosophers for decades. There is a big difference between what the body feels and what the brain perceives as pain. No two pain experiences are alike and no two people react in the same way. Considering how common the pain experience is in daily life, there is still a great deal that is not known about it and while medical science is developing wonder drugs to control pain, it can't be eliminated entirely. So when a patient says she is in pain, a doctor must make a decision about how much painkiller to prescribe. Everyone has a different response to pain, and your own response may change from day to day depending on the circumstance. The body has its own natural painkillers to draw on, which are more powerful than any drugs. You may not even notice scraped knuckles while turning a screwdriver until the job is done. On the other hand, anticipation of pain, such as a visit to the dentist, can seem excruciating before the needle even touches your gums. For me, living on that beach in the Philippines, discomfort and pain were kept at bay by distraction.

By day two, the burning discomfort from the insect bites was replaced thanks to my second mistake as a city slicker, lack of water. The canteen I carried was much too small to meet the thirst on a sun-baked beach. Nothing else matters when you run out of water in the tropics. All your energy is directed towards finding a drink and the longer it takes, the more desperate you become. It was time to find out just how deserted the island really was. Donning my hiking boots and long pants and with a canteen slung over my shoulder I began trekking over the island to see if anyone was living on the other side. Leaving the constant ocean breeze of the beach behind I headed off into the forest where the midday heat was immediately stifling. The islands are extinct volcanoes which gives them steep sides. Every step was a step up. Within minutes I was sweating so profusely I knew I would expire without water. I turned back to the beach. At least a swim would cool me off.

The old saying, Water, water everywhere . . . kept running through my head but it didn't ease the thirst. At the end of the beach a rocky headland rose out of the sea like a knife; I thought there would likely be another beach on the other side, perhaps one with people.

Fortunately I carried a mask and snorkel with me which made it relatively easy to swim long-distance. With the canteen around my shoulder I dove through the surf and began working my way around the rocky outcrop.

The look of surprise on the faces of the three young men working on the other side was well worth the effort. They halted their work on a stone fence and stared mouths open at a sunburnt guy crawling out of the ocean with no boat in sight. "Where did you come from?' they asked.

"I'm Canadian," I said just for the effect, "and boy, was that a long swim!"

They continued staring.

I stared at the sight of their bottle of drinking water, which they were happy to share along with a few travel stories. The drink was enormously refreshing but as they say, give a man a fish and you feed him for a day, give him a net and you feed him for life. I needed my own supply of water not just a drink. They told me that there was no lake or spring on the island but there was a village on the other side where people used cisterns to gather rainwater for drinking. I thanked them for the information and the drink then headed back into the ocean from where I had come. It was the best entrance and exit I had ever made.

The effort of swimming back to my campsite made me almost as thirsty as I had been before I left so the problem was far from solved, but at least I knew that I could find people. Taking shelter under the trees I waited out the mid-day Sun before packing up and resuming my overland trek. Even though the early evening air was slightly cooler, my thirst continued to nag at the back of my throat with an insistence I couldn't ignore. It's astounding how the body sends such an irresistible message when it comes to water. We can survive for a week without food, but only a few days without a drink and as the thirst builds, nothing else matters.

At the top of the hill I began to wonder how much moisture I had lost through perspiration. Too bad that water is salty. I propped my backpack against the base of a coconut tree and reclined for a rest when a glorious realization washed over me. The answer to my thirst had been within reach all along, I just hadn't recognized it . . . coconut milk. There, hanging directly over my head, were three or four large green coconuts, hopefully ripe enough to be filled with that lovely sweet liquid.

The islanders obviously harvest the coconuts because a series of crescent-shaped slashes had been cut into the side of the tree trunk making it easy to climb up the ten metres to the top. I grabbed the half-metre-long knife with the curved blade I had bought from a Sherpa in the mountains of Nepal and tucked it into my belt pirate-style and began the climb in earnest. Isn't it funny how everything always looks farther away when you look down than when you look up? Coconut trees are very tall.

The tree trunk was about a metre and a half across at the base, more than I could wrap my arms around. But thanks to the footholds slashed in the sides, and the fact that there are no branches all the way up, it was a fairly easy telephone-pole type of climb, although I did notice that the Filipinos take very large steps. By the time I reached the top, where all the giant palm leaves sprout upwards like cathedral arches, the trunk had narrowed down to a small enough circumference so I could just reach around and hold on with my right arm and cut the coconut with the left.

I was now faced with the challenge of choosing which of the three green coconuts nestled among the palm leaves was the most likely to contain milk. Not knowing anything about coconuts I chose the largest which unfortunately was almost out of reach around the other side of the trunk. There wasn't much room to manoeuvre around since it was taking most of my strength just to hang on with one hand like a telephone lineman without a safety belt. Even though my knife blade was half a metre long, the combination of bad angle and no swing room made the blade almost ineffective against the stem holding the coconut in place. After repeated strikes I managed to reduce the stem to one stubborn strand that just wouldn't let go. It was too flexible for the knife to do any more damage. Meanwhile the muscles in my right arm were beginning to scream from fatigue. If they let go I would drop out of the tree before the coconut. Replacing the knife in its holster I figured I could just yank my prize out of its lair with my hand. The problem was getting to it. Extending to the full limit of my reach around the trunk I could just get four fingers over the top of the coconut. With all the effort I could muster I bore down with one huge jerk and watched to my delight as the stubborn fruit dropped away and made a seemingly slow, one-second flight to the ground, landing with a solid thud. Success at last. But the joy of harvesting my first coconut was immediately cut by a searing pain from my left shoulder. I looked over at the shocking sight of my upper arm slumped down below the joint, dangling at an odd angle from the side of my body. The shoulder had dislocated.

There are documented cases where people have suffered severe wounds, even lost limbs and felt nothing at all. The nervous system has the ability to shut off overwhelming signals from a large injury like a circuit breaker that trips when too much current runs through wires.

My mind raced into overdrive with a flurry of thoughts: ouch, pain . . . I'm all alone, pain, there is no hospital nearby, more pain, I don't even know where the village is, jabbing pain, what happens if it doesn't go back in, throbbing pain, never felt so much pain before, getting hotter, still thirsty, getting dizzy . . . then the question that struck terror in my heart, cleared my head and made the pain seem to disappear: how am I going to get down from this tree with one arm?

I pictured myself falling ten metres to the ground, lying broken at the bottom of the tree for days or even weeks. Help seemed very far away. Was my life going to end here in pursuit of a coconut?

Suddenly the pain became secondary under the realization that I was in a very serious predicament. The next few minutes saw a strength of willpower I have not experienced since. There was no choice in the matter, I had to get down the tree fast and I needed both arms to do it. The whole tree trunk was leaning slightly to one side forming a long arc curving upwards. I had climbed up along the topside of the trunk and knew if I tried to slide down with one arm my body would slip around to the underside and I wouldn't be able to hold my own weight.

Somehow the dislocated arm still worked even though it was sticking out at an odd direction. I was able to wrap it around the trunk and allow the fear of falling to overcome the pain from the shoulder while I slid down the tree trunk in one continuous motion using both arms for support.

In extreme emergencies, the brain needs to put the pain aside so it can deal with the situation that caused the pain. In the past, when that situation could have meant being chased by a lion or pack of hyenas, it was more important to get to safety rather than lie down wailing in pain. Running with an injured limb normally generates more pain, but in an emergency, the brain sends out a flood of endorphins, powerful drugs related to morphine that stop the pain signals so the body can move. Scientists call this "stress-induced analgesia," part of our natural defence system.

There were no wild animals chasing me, but I was still in considerable danger. If the arm stayed out of joint for too long, it could do damage to the ligaments and tendons, perhaps render my arm useless for life. I had to deal with it then and there.

Stepping away from the base of the tree, thankful to at least be on the ground, I stood staring at the limb, which began to appear foreign. An out-of-place limb looks like some new appendage that has been shoved into the side of your body like a log through the side of a house.

The fear of falling from the tree had now been replaced by the fear of losing the use of my most valuable arm—I'm left-handed. I had two choices, either leave it that way and try to find help, or try to get it back in the joint myself. The idea of leaving my arm dislocated for a long period was terrifying. What would happen, would it get worse, would it become infected or diseased, would I be deformed for life?

Remembering a conversation about dislocated joints, I curled my right hand into a fist, shoved it up under the arm and pushed upwards hard. While manoeuvring the shoulder in a circular motion there came the most sickening sound of gristle grinding in the joint which suddenly clunked back into place. "You lucky bastard," I muttered to myself as miraculously I was able to move the arm freely and my shoulder looked like a shoulder again.

The relief was so profound I had completely forgotten about the pain. In fact, I can't remember any pain at all during the entire slide down the tree trunk and relocating the joint with my fist. As I rubbed it and moved it around there was nothing more than a dull sensation but even that was quickly replaced by the sensation that had driven me up the tree in the first place . . . thirst. The effort of climbing three storeys up the tree, hacking with the knife and performing emergency first aid had raised my temperature and thirst to new levels of intensity. I still didn't know if the coconut had milk in it.

My tree experience was just one example of the many ways the brain has to control pain. Opiate-related chemicals released by my brain temporarily eliminated the pain so it wouldn't interfere with getting out of the emergency. Studies of patients in emergency wards have shown that at least a third do not actually feel any pain. The combination of shock, embarrassment or even fear of lost wages overpowers any sensation of pain. Many don't feel a thing until eight or nine hours later. Endorphins are powerful natural opiates. They are released by the brain almost as a calming effect so attention can be focused on solving the crisis.

Our skin is our largest organ, covering about three square metres. It also provides our first contact with the world and our primary sensory input after the eyes. When the skin is touched the sensation is sent to the brain as a pattern, depending on whether the touch was soft, hard and how much area of the skin came in contact. This is an incredibly delicate system, responding to everything from a gentle breeze to a strike from a heavy object. How a sensation turns into pain is a very inexact science because everyone has a different tolerance level. The exact pathway to the brain is not completely understood either but there are at least two different highways pain can take on its journey from the skin to whatever part of the brain says ouch. Nerve fibres come in two sizes, large and small, and they are responsible for two different types of pain messages.

The large fibres respond to stronger sensations and are very good at locating the site of the pain. Their important message travels more quickly than the small fibres but they also trigger another effect that can block their message before it gets to the brain. In 1965 Reginald Melzack, a Canadian pain researcher at McGill University in Montreal, developed the gate control theory. Along with a British scientist named Patrick Wall he proposed that a series of nerve pathways in your spinal cord can turn off a pain signal when the signal is too strong. These gates look something like butterfly wings with four segments and they run the full length of the spinal column like the angular plates that ran down the back of a stegosaurus, except our gates are made of nerves. The gates contain large fibres, which respond to gentle touch, as well as small fibres, which only turn on if the stimulus is intense. The large fibres can close the gate if the sensation is powerful enough; the small fibres open them. This race to deliver the message of pain to the brain is one of the reasons a small injury can feel more painful than a larger one.

When someone rubs your skin with a silk scarf the large fibres are stimulated, sending a signal up to the brain that translates into a pleasant sensation. The large fibres are very good at locating where that sensation happens on the skin, allowing you to savour every fold in the silk as it caresses the hollow of your back. The small fibres are not stimulated by the scarf at all. Now suppose your teasing partner decides to get a little more aggressive and begins swatting you with a paddle. The first slap will trigger the small fibres which will open the gates and send a pain message directly to the brain. The first slap always seems to hurt most. If the slapping continues the large fibres, which can send their signals faster, overtake the small ones and close the gate so the sensation of pain will not continue to rise beyond unbearable levels. Meanwhile the small fibres are still being stimulated and try to reopen the gate to let the pain message through. A type of preprocessing happens at the gate to filter the messages to the brain. Whether or not the message gets through depends on the severity and continuation of the pain message.

On the beach, the insects did a very good job of stimulating my small fibres and keeping the pain gates open to the brain. Bug bites are not severe enough to make the large fibres close the gate but those large fibres do a very good job of locating exactly where the pesky little critters were feasting on my blood. I tried hiding in my sleeping bag to avoid the biting insects but the tropical air was so warm I couldn't stand to be wrapped in goose down designed for sub-arctic temperatures. After a fitful night of scratching I realized why people in the tropics build their houses on stilts.

My next challenge was getting that drink.

We all have pain in our lives. Today, mine comes mainly from misguided adventures, such as climbing a coconut tree on a remote island in the Philippines, but there was a time when I had no choice. One of the disadvantages of growing up in a low-income family is the lack of health care, especially care of teeth. Everyone who meets me in person immediately notices my unique smile which has prompted more than one person to ask why I haven't had my teeth straightened. One reason is because believe it or not, my teeth have already had a great deal of work done just to keep them in my head. None of it was very pleasant, so the idea of spending more time in a dentist's chair just for cosmetic purposes is not very appealing. Both my parents lost all their teeth so there was neither the dental experience nor the finances available to send any of us children to the dentist. I didn't see a dentist's chair until my late teens when my girlfriend, tired of listening to me complain of constant toothaches, forced me to go have a tooth pulled. Since then I'm embarrassed to say how many other teeth I've lost or had filled but the entire sordid affair has been a remarkable demonstration of pain management.

In fact I didn't appreciate how much pain I was living with until it stopped. Toothaches go right to the root of your skull. They evolve from sharp, icy stabs down the root of the tooth into dull soreness along the jawline into a head-numbing throb that makes you want to rip the side of your face off your skull. At other times it would completely disappear until I made a sudden head movement or bit down on an orange seed. I learned not to turn my head too quickly so my brain could keep up with the motion. It actually felt like my brain was loose inside my skull, sloshing around like an ice cube in a glass, clinking against the sides so hard my vision blurred.

The most powerful pain-management strategy I discovered was distraction. My ears could be ringing with pain but once I sat in a movie theatre or had a difficult job to do, the pain seemed to vanish completely. Through it all, the powerful influence of the mind continued to make the pain appear and disappear like a phantom passing in and out of my head.

Having been through many extractions, I now find the tactics used by dentists interesting and a somewhat effective tool to turn what I used to call pain into discomfort. That doesn't mean I like it any better, but it certainly helps reduce the anxiety. When I now sit in the dentist's chair, I'm the one asking questions about the technology, how fast does the drill spin, how does the anesthetic work, what is the filling made of. These distractions, along with the remarkable advancements in dentistry, have even begun to reduce the discomfort level . . . somewhat. The pain may be less but it's still not a pleasant experience.

A recent experience of having a wisdom tooth pulled introduced me to another trick of pain management, "diffuse noxious inhibitory control," otherwise known as pain inhibits pain. The offending tooth was on the upper right side—you know, the spot where the roots seem to go right into your brain. I've had teeth removed under a variety of conditions, the most difficult for the dentist being my kicking and fighting in the chair to an assortment of sedatives, the mild buzz of nitrous-oxide gas, the more powerful rush from assorted narcotics injected into my veins and the very strange sensation of closing my eyes for less than one second and finding myself alone in another room, the mental edit of a general anesthetic. Dr. Phillips, the surgeon doing the wisdom-tooth extraction, could provide any of them and suggested none at all because there were no complications. Despite my apparent tolerance for pain, I was considering sedation, which is basically a narcotic that doesn't knock you unconscious but it does provide a buzz powerful enough to provide a distraction. After further consideration I chose nitrous-oxide gas.

For my distraction, I paid attention to how the medical team was trying to distract me. It turned out that the doctor was a big fan of "Quirks and Quarks." The young assistant had never heard of it, so a great discussion arose about the merits of the show, with several questions directed at me. Of course, with a mouth half-frozen and a gas nozzle covering my nose, the responses came out in that distorted language only dentists can understand. Or perhaps they don't understand at all, they just want to keep your mind busy.

By the time the moment of truth arrived I had been intentionally hyperventilating on the gas to get as much effect as possible. "OK doc, I've got the buzz, let's go for it," I said confidently, believing I was master of my own mind. With steady skill his hands swiftly directed a needle into my gums. I inhaled harder. On the next breath he was in with the grippers for the first tug. Another inhalation through my nose. He mutters a word I don't understand to the assistant who says in a loud voice, "OK, you're going to feel a pinprick, just a little pain" . . . and with those words she shoves another needle into the side of my gum through the roof of my mouth. It was a surprise. It was also very sharp and seemed to be on its way through the top of my skull. All it took was one or two seconds of this distraction and everything was over. I never felt the tooth extraction at all: one sensation had completely taken over another, sort of like stubbing your toe to take your mind off the thumb you just hit with a hammer.

Dentists have tapped into another of the body's natural defences against pain—a new pain inhibits the old one. This could be one of the secrets to acupuncture and it is used to treat chronic pain when drugs no longer work.

The biggest issue in pain management is the decision process doctors go through every time a patient complains about pain. How much pain is the person actually feeling: is it enough to inject drugs into the body or is the person simply a hypochondriac who complains about everything?

Trying to understand the relationship between what the body experiences and what the brain feels is the domain of Dr. Gary Rollman, an experimental psychologist at the University of Western Ontario. Using a number of clever devices to inflict just enough pain on his subjects to explore the boundaries between harmless sensations, discomfort and pain, he is interested in why everyone has a different tolerance for pain even when the source of the pain is exactly the same. His torture tools were simple but effective devices designed to produce sensations that start out barely noticeable then gradually increase until they develop into something you really don't want to put up with too much longer. I spent a morning in his lab experiencing an interesting assortment of sensations and exploring the threshold of what we call pain.

During my visit as a reporter for "Morningside," I had already been pinched in the finger by a sharp point pressed against the fingernail, submerged my arm in a bucket of ice water and was now receiving a series of electric shocks into my hand. With each test Dr. Rollman recorded how long it took me to reach the different levels of pain and advised me not to be macho about it because he really wasn't looking for heroes. I didn't last too long under the pressure on my finger or my arm in the ice water, even though Dr. Rollman told me that some of his subjects can last for minutes. That's the first boundary called pain detection, where what you notice is unpleasant but bearable. If the torture victim, or rather "willing volunteer," agrees, the feeling grows until it reaches the second boundary, the threshold of pain. That's the point where you identify it as pain but haven't started screaming yet. Finally, depending on the willingness of the volunteer, the pain continues to climb to the limit of pain tolerance where we say "Stop," "Get this damn thing off me!" or whatever else gets the message across including gestures. Fortunately, Dr. Rollman always ends the experiment at that point, both as a courtesy for his brave volunteers and for his own protection.

The electric shocks were a different kind of experience because I was fascinated by the action of my hand moving entirely on its own. My hand twitched like a sleeping dog having a bad dream. Watching it pulsate once every second, twitching at the wrist and flopping on the table, it looked like something out of an Edgar Allan Poe story, a hand that wouldn't die; fingers leap to my throat and wrestle me to the floor, strangled by my own appendage . . . OK, it wasn't that dramatic, but it certainly didn't feel like my own hand because I had nothing to do with its spasmodic movements. A small electrode attached to my thumb sent tiny shocks into the nerves causing the muscles to contract with every pulse, since the nerve has sensory fibres which convey information about touch and pain to the brain, as well as motor fibres which carry information from the brain down to the muscles. Little lightning bolts darted under my skin, similar to the pins and needles from a foot that has fallen asleep from sitting in the wrong position, except these needles were travelling up my arm along the sensory fibres.

As the voltage increased, the motor fibres began responding as well and my fingers began opening and closing as if I were squeezing a ball. By the time the pins and needles were shooting all the way up to my shoulder I still hadn't identified the sensation as pain, I was too distracted by the strangeness of it all. I asked how much further he could go and Dr. Rollman said, "You've reached the limit, I can't turn it up any further." The distraction of watching my hand twitch had taken my mind off the discomfort, the very essence of the psychology of pain.

When a pain signal arrives at the brain, it goes to the sensory cortex, which is like an alarm going off, but then higher areas of the brain interpret that information and decide how to react to it. That makes pain management a difficult task for doctors because there is such a difference between one person and another. As the old joke goes, "Doctor, my arm hurts when I do this." "Then don't do that." Physicians try to figure out how much pain a person is actually in and how much medication to prescribe. According to Dr. Rollman, people generally fall into two categories, "copers and catastrophizers." I'm apparently in the first category which worked to my advantage as I tried to get milk out of the coconut.

A coconut husk is a heart-shaped fibrous wrapping about the size of a football. Having never opened one before I don't know where to start so I begin hacking away at the top with my Nepalese knife. There is an easy way and a hard way into a husk; of course I am going about it the hard way, slashing across the husk instead of along its length. Sweat is dripping from my forehead by the time I extract the dark, round nut from the mess of fibres. I hold it up to my ear and shake gently. The wonderful sound of liquid sloshing inside is a symphony of sweetness. The next step is breaking through the hard shell of the nut without losing the precious treasure inside. Smashing it on a rock is not a good idea so I continue hacking at the nut with the big knife.

It seems to take an eternity of chipping away at the brown shell, as though this coconut is going to make me work as hard as possible for my drink. Finally a sliver of white appears, pure white, the most beautiful white I have ever seen. Carefully, using the tip of my Swiss Army knife, I bore a tiny hole through the white coconut meat and slowly bring it up to my nose. No foul odours assault my senses. The milk is fresh.

Drinking from the side of a ball is a little clumsy. Some of the white liquid dribbles down my cheek, but those drops are joined by tears of joy that run down my face as the sweetest, most gloriously tasting coconut milk runs across my tongue and quenches the fires of thirst burning at the back of my parched throat.

The crisis is over. The rest of the coconut provides a meal, I have overcome thirst and more astoundingly, overcome pain. In fact, as I watch the Sun set from that hilltop I feel no pain at all . . . intoxicated with the joy of surviving one day in paradise.

Friends will be less fortunate years later when we all experience a different kind of high adventure—trying to fly without wings.

TERMINAL VELOCITY

Deadly serious lessons in skydiving

A DISTURBING THOUGHT nagged at the back of my mind . . . next Thursday, my life could end. Perhaps there was good reason to have those feelings: Thursday was the day I was to step out of a perfectly good airplane ten thousand feet in the air, with no experience, very little instruction and no parachute. Actually, I would be attached to an instructor wearing a parachute big enough to hold both of us. My introduction to skydiving would become one of the most profound and exciting experiences of my life. Little did I know just how close I would come to making it the last experience of my life.

Tandem skydiving is a relatively new sport where two people jump out of a plane with only one parachute. Both the chute and harnesses are designed to carry two people, so it's a long way from the stunts in movies where one person jumps out with no parachute at all and is handed one in the air. Tandem jumping is parachuting's equivalent to bungee jumping, where a paying customer can experience the excitement of the sport without having to be an expert. It's also the only way to experience free fall on your very first jump. Normally parachuting students jump from low altitude using a static line, which is attached to the plane and opens the parachute automatically as soon as the person steps into the air. It usually takes dozens of static line jumps before a high-altitude free fall is allowed. But all tandem jumps begin at 3,000 metres (10,000 feet), providing thirty seconds of free fall before the chute is opened manually by the instructor. My jump would be made before television cameras under the guise of explaining the science involved in parachuting, but actually I just wanted to experience the unnatural feat of human flight. Thrill seekers all over North America have enjoyed the experience, but no matter how much I rationalized about the safety of parachute equipment, the thought of something going wrong was becoming louder and louder in my mind as the day approached. Is there some mechanism in our minds that has foresight? I don't really believe in premonitions; it was probably just good old common sense speaking.

I had convinced the CBC to record my jump for the television show "Wonderstruck," which I was hosting at the time. There is a lot of science involved in terminal velocity, the speed of falling objects, and parachutes have evolved so much that they fly almost as well as airplanes. I intended to explain all these principles of aerodynamics by using myself as the falling object. I really just wanted to experience skydiving. The managers weren't crazy about one of their national hosts jumping out of a plane but after I convinced them that parachute technology has become as safe as any other type of flying, they reluctantly agreed. As more and more people became involved in the shoot, my options for backing out became more limited, which was fine because the excitement of a completely new experience outweighed any trepidations. Skydiving was one of my old dreams so if it ended in catastrophe at least I would be going out doing something really exciting rather than choking on a peanut-butter sandwich.

Still, a nagging thought of something going wrong kept welling up in the back of my mind, growing stronger every day. I could usually brush it off with logic but it began to bother me so much I decided to come to terms with it alone in my boat drifting for a couple of hours in the middle of Lake Ontario. It's an interesting exercise to seriously ask yourself what it would mean if you knew your life would end in a few days. It forces you to look at what you have done up to that point in your life, how you feel about what you've done and how many unfulfilled dreams are left over.

As I thought about how fortunate I'd been to travel around the world, meet so many interesting people and cram more into my short life than many people twice my age, the anxieties about ending it all in a few days settled down. Maybe it was denial that anything would actually go wrong, maybe it's the adrenaline rush that thrill seekers crave when they participate in extreme sports, but eventually a powerful feeling of calm washed over me. We could all lose our lives at any moment by simply crossing the street or being in the wrong place during a shootout at a bank. If I was indeed facing the ultimate deadline, then I would live every remaining minute to the fullest. Besides, my faith in the laws of physics and the technology of parachuting placed the odds in my favour. Sailing back to shore I noticed how much brighter and more beautiful the day had become.

The science of skydiving is pretty straight forward . . . fall as long as possible then slow down just before hitting the ground. You simply let the laws of gravity take over your body for a while. But a funny thing happens to that law when you fling yourself into the air: it doesn't work the way the laws of gravity say it should. Ever since Galileo dropped objects of different size off the Leaning Tower of Pisa, we've been told that all objects should fall at the same speed because gravity acts on all objects in the same way. But look around and you will see everyday examples of how that principle doesn't seem to work. Leaves fall from trees much more slowly than coconuts. It appears that big, heavy objects fall faster than small, light ones. After all, gravity pulls more strongly on massive objects—that's why they feel heavy, right? A feather doesn't have as much mass so it doesn't feel as much gravitational force, therefore it should fall more slowly. So does that mean Galileo was wrong?

Not at all. As usual in science and mathematics, there is a catch. True, massive objects experience more gravitational force, but it also takes more force to move a massive object. A car is harder to push than a bicycle because the car's extra mass gives it more inertia, the tendency to stay put. Gravity acts with less force on the bicycle, but the bicycle is easier to move because it has less mass. So there is always a balance between the amount of gravitational force and the force it takes to move it. That's why, according to theory, all objects should fall at the same speed. But they don't, at least not on Earth.

Only one experiment has ever been conducted on another world that conclusively proved this theory of gravity and that happened on the Moon. Near the end of the *Apollo 15* mission, just before climbing back into the lunar module, Jim Irwin turned to the television camera and said, "We wouldn't be here if it wasn't for a man named Galileo, who said that all objects fall at the same speed. Well, what better place to prove that than here on the Moon."

He then pulled a falcon feather out of a pocket in his space suit. Their lunar lander was named *Falcon*. In his other hand he held a geological hammer. Then, before a world audience he performed the most elegant home science demo ever. Holding the hammer and feather at arm's length in front of his body, he let them both go at the same time. The feeble one-sixth gravity of the Moon made their fall seem slow and lazy but sure enough, after a one-second drop, the feather and the hammer hit the ground at exactly the same time.

"How about that!" said Irwin, almost as though he didn't believe it himself. Galileo was right after all.

The *Apollo* astronauts noticed the same effect in the strange behaviour of the dust as they hopped around on the lunar surface. Each time they took a step, their boots kicked up a layer of fine dust. But rather than form into little billowing clouds, all the particles flew the same distance regardless of their size, forming flat sheets of dust that fell in a ring in front of their boots. The next time you see footage of astronauts walking on the Moon look carefully at their feet and you will see the strange effect, proof that the Moon landings were not simulated in a studio.

So if all objects fall at the same speed on the Moon, why don't they do that on Earth? If Jim Irwin tried his experiment at home the hammer would beat the feather to the ground every time. The difference is air. The only force working on falling objects on the Moon is gravity so everything does fall at the same speed. On Earth, the speed you reach during a fall depends as much on your shape as your mass. That's the concept of terminal velocity and why jumping out of an airplane doesn't feel like falling.

Anything that moves through the air meets resistance because the air has to be pushed out of the way. The more air that is moved, and the higher the speed of the object, the higher the air resistance. Designers of cars and airplanes try to reduce this effect by making the vehicles as narrow as possible. They call it reducing the frontal area. Stand in front of a car and look at how much of the car is actually visible. If the car has good aerodynamics, you won't see much of the vehicle. A truck has a larger frontal area because speed is not as important as carrying capacity. Look at a fighter jet face on and the plane almost disappears. Air resistance is a major force at supersonic speeds so fighters are built with thin wings and narrow fuselage to cut through the air as effortlessly as possible.

Falling objects encounter the same air resistance because every second they fall, gravity accelerates them up to higher and higher speeds. But as the speed increases so does the resistance of the air. Eventually the force of the air trying to slow the object down matches the force of gravity trying to speed it up. That's terminal velocity, when the object continues to fall but it doesn't fall any faster. Feathers fall slowly because they have a large surface area for the air to work on but not much mass for gravity. Rocks have a lot of mass concentrated into a small area so gravity dominates and they fall much faster. Rocks still have a terminal velocity; it's just a lot higher than feathers. The highest terminal velocity reached by a human was in 1960 when Colonel Joe Kittinger stepped out of a balloon at 31,333 metres (102,800 feet). At that altitude the air is so thin it did not even flap his uniform. He fell for thirteen minutes with so little air resistance that he almost broke the sound barrier with his body. Once he entered the thicker air of the lower atmosphere his terminal velocity dropped enough that he was able to open his chute without tearing it to shreds.

At lower altitudes, it only takes five or six seconds to reach a terminal velocity of about 250 km/h. Not all parachutists reach that speed. Beginners and many military jumpers use a static line which attaches the rip cord to the airplane so the chute opens immediately. Those jumps are made just a few thousand feet above ground. I would be making a free jump, where we step out into empty space at 3,000 metres (10,000 feet), fall freely at terminal velocity for thirty seconds, or six thousand feet, whichever happens first, then open the parachute, increase our surface area by about a hundred times and let the air resistance lower that velocity to about 10 km/h for a soft landing. That's the principle. Actually trying it with your own body is another matter altogether.

On jump day I was primed and ready when we arrived at the parachute club. My instructor, or should I say carrier, Steve West, was a friendly, lanky fellow who had logged thousands of hours in the air without an airplane. His calm manner inspired confidence, something vital in this exercise where my life would be entirely in his hands. Steve was more than just a professional skydiver, he was the regional inspector who certified other people's parachutes to ensure they were safe for jumping. He would be making all the decisions in the air including when to open the parachute, and what to do in case it didn't open.

Amazingly, there are choices to be made when something goes wrong during a parachute jump. The first thing a parachutist does after opening the rip cord is look up and make sure the chute is fully open. If it's tangled in the lines and flapping like a flag, the first thing to do is stay calm, even though you are plunging towards the ground at a terrific rate, then vigorously shake the lines. Often, when a chute fails to unfold properly, giving the lines a good shake is enough to untangle the fabric and fill it with air. If that fails, there is always the emergency chute, which is equipped with an altitude sensor that automatically pops it below three thousand feet. Hopefully we weren't going to explore either of those choices on the day of my jump.

There isn't a great deal of preparation for a tandem jump. I was expecting to leap off towers and learn how to roll my body on landing. Instead, Steve hands me a tight-fitting nylon jumpsuit, a soft leather helmet, goggles and an intricate harness that wraps around my thighs, waist and over my shoulders. The jumpsuit fits over my clothing to keep the fabric from flapping, the helmet prevents my hair from beating against my forehead, goggles let me see the view and the harness keeps me attached to Steve. This is the same harness worn by parachutists except there is no parachute attached to it. Four stainless steel clips, two on the shoulders and two on the hips, attach to Steve's harness so we effectively become one body attached to the parachute. Essentially I wear Steve on my back while he wears the parachute on his back. That allows him the freedom to take care of all the business while I go along for an unobstructed front-seat view of the jump.

"What about the landing?" I ask

"Don't worry about that," he replies calmly. "I'll show you all that on the way down."

Talk about on-the-job training . . .

Our ferry to 3,000 meters (10,000 feet) is a twin-engine Piper that has had its rear seats and door removed. Steve and I; Steve's wife, also a jumper; Kelvin Brundrett, wearing a helmet-mounted camera; and a CBC cameraman who isn't going to jump are all huddled together on the floor. It takes about fifteen minutes to make the climb and it's during that pause in the action when all those nagging thoughts return to my head. As we bounce down the grass runway and start the climb into the sky, I realize that from this point on our lives will depend totally on a thin sheet of nylon tightly packed into a bundle on Steve's back. Of course I could still call the whole thing off but it is clear that Steve wants to live until tomorrow, so the risk is obviously pretty low.

Technically speaking, the chances of dying from skydiving are far lower than getting killed in a car accident. Besides, the technology of parachutes has been tested and proven for almost a hundred years, so I might as well enjoy the ride.

The only way to describe the following ten minutes is a movie where the scenes change really fast. Scene 1 is inside the crowded plane on our knees with our backs to the open door. I manoeuvre myself against Steve so he can attach the clips from my harness to his. The pilot throttles back the engines to slow the plane down and we begin looking for our landing spot. That first glance at the ground is quite disconcerting because it looks very far away. More than three kilometres of air separate us from the ground.

Kelvin, wearing his helmet-cam, is the first out the door. He crawls along the outside of the airplane towards the tail and lies spread-eagle along the fuselage waiting for the rest of us. He records our departure and stays with us during free fall. Steve and I crawl backwards into the doorway, grab the rain gutter along the top edge, then stand up.

Scene 2. I'm now getting an extreme close-up of the outside of an airplane. My face is against the top of the body, the wind is blowing about as hard as the breeze I feel riding a motorcycle along the highway. To my left, Kelvin is sprawled across the tail of the plane grinning widely. To my right is the white roof of the plane, with the low wing and one of the engines just visible over the curving shape. The propeller is turning so slowly I can see the blades. Steve yells in my ear with instructions to bend my knees and put my feet back between his legs. I fold my arms across my chest so I'm completely dangling off Steve's chest while he stands in the doorway holding my entire weight. Kelvin loses his grip on the smooth body of the plane and falls off the tail. No problem, this is skydiving and he has his own parachute. Steve immediately lets go, faces the front of the plane and steps into thin air.

Scene 3. The plane instantly disappears, replaced by an all-encompassing blue sky. The sound of the wind increases but under the soft helmet and goggles it streams past without turbulence, a velvety flow that supports our bodies like a billion feathers. Humanity's oldest dream is to fly freely like the birds. Amazingly, the sensation of letting go of an airplane at ten thousand feet doesn't feel like leaping off a diving board, or dropping over the first hill of a roller coaster; in fact, it doesn't feel like falling at all. Your body feels like it's floating upon a soft pillow of air suspended in a great blue space. It really is a sensation of flight.

It takes about six seconds to reach terminal velocity, where our speed becomes constant. The air pushes harder against my chest, creating the sensation of slowing down rather than speeding up. It's not stepping into thin air at all; it acts like a soft hand holding you up. When our speed stabilizes the sensation of movement stops, the same way you only feel the initial drop of an elevator ride then feel nothing as it moves at a steady speed down the shaft. Suspended out there in that very large blue space there are no visible signs of falling. Even the land below, a checkerboard pattern of farmers' fields, doesn't appear to get any closer. From ten thousand feet the distance is too great to see any quick changes in perspective.

For thirty seconds, we enjoy the unusual experience of human flight. It's not very elegant, with our arms and legs spread out like crabs, but with slight twists of the body we could change our position slightly. To my surprise, Kelvin appears flying in front of us with camera rolling. Even though he left the plane first, he waited for us in the air. Skydivers change their speed by altering their body shape. He has spread himself out as much as possible to increase his air resistance and slow down. Then I feel a tug on my right arm. Steve's wife, who left the plane after us, is flying alongside. She has put herself into a nosedive to catch up to us, then spread her arms and legs to slow down and fly in formation. I've never had a human fly over to me and shake hands before.

Thirty seconds flies by pretty fast, especially when you are flying fast yourself. Steve waves off our flying partners, who back away to a safe distance. Reaching into a small pocket on his leg, Steve grabs a small drogue chute and tosses it out behind. The drogue pulls the main chute out of the pack and our terminal velocity changes from 200 km/h to almost zero in about three seconds.

Scene 4. If you've ever watched a baby bouncing up and down in a Jolly Jumper, that's what it feels like when the parachute opens. There is no sudden jerk, it's just one huge pull upwards as the canopy fills with air. We are actually still falling downwards but it feels like we have reversed direction because the other jumpers fall quickly below us and a very strong force pulls on the harness straps wrapped around my legs. The parachute is designed to open gradually so it doesn't rip your arms and legs off. The slow opening also protects the thin nylon fabric from being torn to shreds. Still, it's quite an abrupt change from flying freely to being lifted by the harness around your thighs and chest until you dangle quietly under a colourful roof of nylon. The quick rush of air becomes a gentle hiss as air whistles through the shrouds and cords that reach skyward to embrace the huge rainbow-coloured canopy. Looking up at that fully inflated parachute is a beautiful sight, proof that the rest of our journey to the ground will be a gentle one.

Our parachute is a rectangular "ram-air" design which actually flies like an airplane. Openings along the leading edge allow air to ram between two layers of fabric, inflating them so the parachute assumes the airfoil shape of a wing. By simply pulling on control lines it can be steered left or right, even speed up or slow down. Steve hands me the two lines and shows me how to steer during our five-minute flight to the ground. Finally, there is time to enjoy the view and let my heart rate return to normal.

Scene 5. The landing target is a ten-metre circle of sand that looks remarkably small from the air. A button about the size of a Frisbee sits in the centre as a bull's eye. Since we are actually flying and not just dropping straight down, we turn downwind then turn again, approaching the landing site facing the wind the way airplanes do. Our goal is to make a perfect stand-up landing exactly in the centre of the target. The idea is to stop the parachute when you are about a metre off the ground and simply stand up. That's the theory. With Steve calling out course corrections and me pulling wildly on the control lines, the ground begins to rush upwards. Of course, timing is everything and I do manage to stop the chute . . . just a little late. It isn't quite a stand-up landing, more of a stumble, skid and fall backwards approach, but as they say, any landing you can walk away from is a good one.

It's impossible to describe the exhilaration of feeling the ground beneath you once again after performing a totally unnatural feat in the air. The fact that we made it, everything worked perfectly and we didn't die is as much a relief as a thrill. I understand why risk-takers become addicted to the rush—there's nothing like going out onto an edge, thumbing your nose at death, then coming back alive.

We made two more jumps that day so the cameras could see the operation from every angle. By the time we were ready to leap from the plane for the final time I knew that if anything was going to go wrong, this was it. Perhaps it was that thought that heightened my senses as we released our grip on safety for the final time. I've never been so acutely aware of every passing second as I was on that final dive. The fact that I'm able to write about the experience and you are reading it proves I didn't die that day, but about a month later, Steve and Kelvin were not so fortunate.

It was another perfect day and they were up in the same airplane with the same parachute taking another eager passenger for a tandem dive. During those awkward moments when everyone is jostling for position in the doorway of the aircraft, the small drogue chute accidentally works its way out of Steve's leg pocket and begins fluttering in the airstream. The nylon cord rips into thin threads that whip about dangerously close to the tail of the aircraft. Steve and Kelvin look at each other with alarm. A quick decision has to be made before the situation worsens. If the main chute pops out while they are still clinging to the airplane, the real trouble begins. They have two choices, either climb back into the plane or jump and deal with the problem in the air. The first option might seem like the obvious choice, but Steve was worried that if he crawled back into the plane, the shredded line and drogue chute could become tangled in the tail of the plane and possibly lead to a crash. Rather than risk the lives of the others in the aircraft, Steve and Kelvin decided to jump clear of the plane and deal with the faulty parachute on the way down. They had less than a minute to live.

The grizzly details of their plunge were recorded by Kelvin's helmet camera. The first thing Steve attempted was to open the main chute, but since the drogue chute was already out and tangled, the main chute became tangled along with it and didn't open completely. Shaking the shrouds to open the fouled parachute didn't work.

The next option is the emergency chute. But first Steve must cut the main chute loose using a knife in a pouch on his other leg. The emergency chute will not open properly until the main chute is thrown clear, otherwise the two become tangled together. The young man attached to Steve's chest realizes something is wrong and begins to panic. He flails his arms about wildly trying to get free. Kelvin flies over to help calm the man down and assist Steve cutting away the fouled parachute. The desperate thrashing of the terrified man eats up precious seconds as the three bodies continue their horrible plunge.

Despite the best efforts of Steve and Kelvin, they cannot clear the chute. At three thousand feet a built-in safety device automatically opens the emergency parachute but with the main chute still attached it does not open fully. They have run out of options. Kelvin stays with the stricken pair longer than he should. He breaks away at the last second but there is simply not enough air between him and the ground for his chute to open fully. All three men lost their lives.

Hearing the news of the accident I returned alone to the middle of Lake Ontario. Images of my own jump made it easy to picture their death fall in vivid detail. Forget what you hear about blacking out before you hit the ground. It's quite the opposite, you become hyper-aware of every detail, especially when you know something is wrong. In the final moments, Steve West and Kelvin Brundrett knew they had reached terminal velocity. Gravity won. Nature has a way of doing that, taking away our friends. When we know that some of the responsibility is our own we can find some consolation knowing that those who died knew they were taking a risk. It's a little harder to accept death when nature just takes and we have no choice in the matter at all.

LABORATORY TO
LIFE SUPPORT

*Research breakthroughs versus
cancer realities*

IT SEEMS I'VE ALWAYS been a champion of science, defender of the scientific method, confident that with enough knowledge and human ingenuity, almost any problem can be overcome. After all, science got us to the Moon and beyond, no problem is too big. Well, some of that faith was shaken when the best medical science in the world was unable to save my best friend.

I found myself living a strange contradiction. During the day I was visiting research hospitals to interview scientists fighting on the front lines in the war on cancer. Each evening I visited another hospital where my best friend was dying from it. It was a hard lesson in reality, where I found the cheery optimism of scientists experimenting in laboratories a long way from real cures that are able to help people with the disease today. I was hoping to learn more about new treatments for cancer and perhaps find a way to help my friend or at least provide some encouraging information about his prospects for survival

Gerry Frisque and I spent our formative adolescent years together when friendships are forged for a lifetime. He was stronger, one of those annoying athletic types who could do

283

almost anything without really trying while the rest of us struggled to keep up. We grew tall, grew out of our clothes, traded bicycles for motorcycles and most importantly, at least at the time, discovered how to deal with the female members of our species. We watched each other suffer through teenage tragedies that come with dreaming about girls, pursuing girls, being rejected by girls, trying to get away from girls. We learned a lot about the world, about ourselves and by the time we were ready to leave high school, believed we had pretty well figured everything out. Through it all, our friendship quietly solidified itself through the simple act of hanging out together.

We headed down different roads after high school, crossing paths at the odd wedding and keeping track of each other's lives from a distance.

It had been more than a decade since I had seen my old friend when I received a phone call from his brother who told me Gerry was in a Toronto hospital waiting for surgery to remove a tumour from his brain. I called immediately. He recognized my voice instantly while I recognized something unfamiliar in his. Words came slowly as though he had to think about every syllable. The slightest hint of a slur crossed his speech.

"Hey man," I quipped. "I always knew you were sick in the head, what's up this time?"

"This is serious man. They've already removed one tumour from my brain; this is the second one, but they think they'll get it all this time."

I knew this was no joke. Digging around inside someone's brain is serious business. "I'll see you tonight," I said.

All old friends reflect the passage of time, but when I walked into the hospital that night I wasn't prepared for the sight of a man my own age who looked like a senior citizen. The bony shape of Gerry's skull showed through the pallor of his face. On the side of his head just behind his right ear a large circular scar larger than a $2 coin marked the spot where they had cut a tumour the size of a golf ball out of his brain. His emaciated features made it seem as if time was passing more quickly for him than the rest of us, ushering his body into old age. I tried not to react to his appearance although I'm sure it showed on my face. Despite his skeletal features, he was still quite positive about his situation.

"I'm getting a special laser treatment this Friday—it's the latest technology. Why don't you come over for a visit in my new house next Tuesday when I get out of here?"

"Sure," I said, although I found it hard to believe he could have his skull opened up, his brain worked on and be back home in a week. He reassured me that his recovery from the first operation was fast and he was determined to get back on his feet just as quickly from this one. I did my best to believe him. At least his positive attitude was a good sign.

I left the hospital with a new appreciation for cancer research. It became more than just science: it became a great hope for my friend's survival.

U.S. president Richard Nixon declared war on cancer in 1971, and the Canadian Cancer Society formed two years later. The military strategy seemed to make sense at that time because Vietnam was on everyone's mind. Cancer was considered an enemy that could be hunted down and destroyed using high-technology weapons. It would be wiped out like polio was in the 1950s. But as the Americans learned while fighting the Viet Cong, high-tech weapons are not as effective on an enemy that constantly changes and hides. Cancer is a wily opponent, fighting a type of guerrilla warfare by constantly changing and adapting itself to avoid our assaults.

The most difficult aspect to deal with is the fact that cancer is not some foreign invader that comes from outside the body, like a cold or flu. If that were the case it would be fairly straightforward to deal with: identify the enemy, develop a vaccine then let our body's immune system take care of it. Or we could find out where it came from and cut it off at the source. But cancer cells do not come from somewhere else, they are part of our own body. For some unknown reason, normal healthy skin, liver, lung, brain or almost any of the trillion cells that make up our body decide they don't want to be normal any more. This happens all the time and most mutants are caught by the body's immune system or forced to commit suicide but some escape detection, forming a rebellion. The rebels wear the same clothes as everyone else so the body police don't know where to find them. The rebellion grows without opposition.

Sometimes the runaway cells cluster in tightly packed groups, or tumours. When the group gets larger, individuals break off from the base camp and spread throughout the body on their own . . . metastasis. The rogue cells establish new colonies in the lymph nodes, bones, liver or brain. Their numbers grow rapidly through continuous reproduction as they double their population over and over again. Like any hungry army, they consume food and resources, starving out the normal residents and taking over their territory. Unnoticed at first then suddenly lethal, the rebellion finally takes over, but nobody wins as the mutants release toxins and destroy essential tissue until the body consumes itself in a destructive, downward, deathly spiral.

"Know your enemy": the military motto is hard to follow with cancer. There are more than one hundred forms of the disease. It can come from anywhere, hiding unnoticed within the body until its numbers become large enough to carry out a surprise attack with deadly force.

When the war on cancer was first declared, three primary weapons were developed to fight the disease: surgery, chemotherapy and radiation treatment. All three take a brute-force approach, by attempting to kill the cancerous cells and eradicate them from the body. But after decades of fighting, these weapons have reached their limit. They kill but they don't eliminate everything. Enough of the enemy survives the assaults to continue spreading. Chemotherapy destroys cancer cells but it also kills normal cells needed to keep the patient healthy, such as those in the gut. At the same time it knocks out the body's immune system, opening up the risk of other infection. If a lump or tumour is visible and compact, a surgeon can cut it out. If it's large, the area around it may be removed as well, such as a breast or underlying muscle. But often the surgeon's knife leaves some cancer cells behind, enough to provide the seeds for further growth. Tumours send out tendrils among surrounding cells like roots of a weed. It doesn't take many leftover roots to grow a new weed. The surgeon can return to remove the new growths, but cutting out pieces of the body can't continue forever. Removing tumours can even upset the balance of growth between healthy and cancerous cells so tumours that were previously dormant suddenly spring to life. Cancer wins.

When the enemy divides and spreads throughout the body through metastasis, hiding from the bayonets of surgeons, chemical warfare takes over. A whole cocktail of toxic chemicals have been developed to poison cancer cells through chemotherapy. They either kill the cells outright or interfere with the process that makes cells divide so they won't grow. Hormones, antibiotics, even mustard gas, used in the trenches of the First World War, all work at different stages of the disease with limited success. Chemotherapy holds the cancer at bay for a time, but it doesn't usually get rid of it.

The benefits of chemotherapy just barely outweigh the costs. These drugs are designed to kill cells, which makes them highly toxic to healthy cells as well. Doctors take great care to try and deliver the chemotherapy to specific areas where the cancer resides, which is almost impossible to do. People still suffer from nausea, loss of hair, hypertension even diabetes as side effects from the drugs.

While this chemical warfare is taking place, there are some cancer cells—and it only takes a few—that are not harmed by the drugs. They have mutated in a way that affords them protection. The mutant survivors become the new cancer that is resistant to further treatment. The doses of chemotherapy must be increased, but there is only so much the patient can take. Eventually cancer wins again.

Our last resort is nuclear warfare, powerful radiation from x-rays or gamma rays which are beamed on the tumours to burn them away. But the line between killing the cancer and killing the patient is not very wide when it comes to these three treatments, which is why cancer is still winning.

The big question on everyone's mind is, "If we've been waging war on this disease for all these years, why haven't we won?" The military approach of slash, poison and burn using bayonets, chemicals and radiation has only won battles but not the war. People are living a little longer with cancer, but death rates from the disease have barely changed since the war began. Sixty thousand Canadians succumbed to the disease in 1998 alone.

Gerry had all three procedures on his head. The tumour had appeared only a year and a half earlier. It was an extremely rare, juvenile type of tumour that usually appears in the stomach or leg muscles of adolescents. How it got into Gerry's brain no one knows. The family wondered if the cancer was related to a severe electrical shock that had almost killed him on a construction site several years earlier. Others thought it might be his never-ending habit of holding a cell phone to his head. But the doctors could find no evidence of a link to electrical fields. Only thirty documented cases like his were on record and all were terminal. Surgeons had been into his head to cut the tumour out but months later it returned. When they explored a second time there were three new ones and the cancer was spreading. Chemotherapy and radiation couldn't stop the growth and now he was back for a third time. The prognosis was not good.

Gerry's condition piqued my interest in cancer research, in particular why we were not winning the war on cancer. The benefit of working on a national science program is having access to some of the top cancer research labs in Canada. While most research is following new tactics, the makers of high-tech weapons have not completely given up. I was particularly interested in the laser that was to be used on Gerry's brain tumour. I found it in the basement of Princess Margaret Hospital in Toronto, where the door to the room seals completely shut so when the lights go out, the darkness is pierced by multicoloured laser beams bouncing through an elaborate set of mirrors and lenses like a scene from a science-fiction movie.

Lasers have been used successfully in medicine for decades. The intense, narrow beams of light carry a lot of energy which can be used to burn unwanted tissue without bleeding. In the 1970s I sat in on eye surgery where a laser zapped tiny blood vessels that had grown inside the eyes of a person with diabetes. Looking through an extra eyepiece alongside the doctor, I was able to look directly into the eye of the patient who sat quietly on the other side of the instrument. No anesthetic was necessary. Covering the back of the eye is the retina, which is the part that we actually see with, the photographic film for the brain. Diabetics sometimes develop extra blood vessels that grow across the retina interfering with vision. The laser treatment prevents the blood vessels from growing further by burning their ends shut.

It was amazing to see a tiny green dot wandering across the retina guided by a joystick in the doctor's hand. When the dot reached a blood vessel there was a tiny flash of green light as the beam pulsed up to full power, leaving behind a small white dot like a spot welder where the blood vessel had been. It was over in less than a second. The beam was guided to another vessel—pop, pop, pop—making about a hundred welds all over the retina with no discomfort to the patient. The whole procedure was over in fifteen minutes.

Lasers do their work using specific colours of light which are turned into heat when they shine on body tissue. Lasers are absorbed only if they shine on something that's a different colour than the beam. Most tissue in the body is red, so blue or green light is often used for treatment. A red laser would be reflected by red tissue so there would be no heat produced. It's the same effect as wearing a black shirt on a sunny day. It absorbs white sunlight making you feel hotter than a white shirt which reflects the light. The trick using lasers for cancer treatment is getting the beam to kill only the cancer cells and not the healthy ones. Cancer cells can be red too.

Dr. Brian Wilson gets around this problem using a dye that paints the cancer cells a darker colour. The dye was designed to stick only to the tumour so the laser beam will only be absorbed by those cells and reflected off the others. Using thin, hair-like fibre optics, the laser beams can be directed to cancer sites within the body. It's a neat idea and Dr . Wilson was optimistic that it would work. When I told him about the laser treatment to be used on Gerry's brain, he said the effectiveness of the laser depends on the depth of the tumour. If it is near the surface the laser will get it. But the beam cannot penetrate too deeply.

When I returned to Gerry's bedside to tell him about it, he was encouraged, then asked me to give him a neck rub to ease his chronic headache. As I stood behind him looking at the scar on side of his skull I tried to see the tumour and imagined the laser beam zapping it away to nothingness, relieving the pressure of my friend's brain. We would find out how effective the laser was in a few days.

The main thrust of cancer research today is away from weapons of mass destruction and towards more precision attacks that get at the fundamental process of cancer itself. Today's researchers are attempting to understand exactly how the disease works, to find the culprits that start the rebellion and to interrupt the process that allows the cells to mutate and spread. In other words, they are trying to find the generals and steal their battle plans rather than shoot at the troops.

The big question is why normal cells in the body suddenly decide to start reproducing out of control. If that triggering mechanism could be stopped, cancer wouldn't appear in the first place. The problem of course is never that simple. Cancer isn't started by one trigger; there is a whole sequence of events that set the disease in motion. One thing is known for sure: cancer is a genetic disease, where something goes wrong in the genes within a cell turning it into a rebel.

Think of a cell as a videocassette containing your all-time

favourite movie, *Star Wars*, for example. All the information for the movie is coiled up on the magnetic tape. The videocassette player reads that information and turns it into sound and pictures. If someone comes along and records an infomercial about psychic healing over your tape, the cassette still looks the same and the player still reads it, but the product has changed dramatically. Genes are bits of information strung along the DNA molecule that is coiled up inside the nucleus of a cell like videotape. The cell, like a video player, reads the information on the genes so it knows what to do for a living, whether it's a lung cell that absorbs oxygen from the air, a liver cell that removes waste from the blood or a brain cell that transmits electrical signals. When genes are changed, or mutated, the cell still looks the same but its instructions have changed so it stops contributing to tissue function and begins reproducing out of control. That's when it's cancerous.

The problem is finding the damaged genes. There are thousands of them in human DNA and hundreds can be involved in cancer. Mutations happen all the time and the body even has a system in place to repair damaged genes, but somehow the repair mechanism breaks down in some people and the damage spreads.

A major breakthrough came in 1994 when a key mutation associated with breast cancer was discovered. Now women with the mutant gene can be screened and monitored closely so the cancer can be treated earlier, when the chances of beating the disease are best. That discovery also opens a whole new approach to fighting cancer, from the inside at the genetic level rather than from the outside with radiation or poisons.

But knowing the gene is not enough. Each form of cancer has a different set of mutant genes at work. The real accomplishment will come when scientists can either repair the

damaged genes or interrupt the process. Work on colon cancer has shown that a single mutation can produce polyps,
which are small growths that look like broccoli lining the
colon. That's not cancerous but it is the first of four other
genetic changes that do lead to cancer.

Unfortunately, the genetic nature of cancer means it can be
passed down through families. Two years earlier Gerry's father
had died of brain cancer in the same hospital. That's not to say
the cancer was inherited; the type of cancer was completely
different. Nonetheless it was tough on the family to see the
same thing happening all over again in the same rooms in the
same hospital because they knew the inevitable result.

One prominent Canadian geneticist who is spearheading
some of the genetic research is Dr. Eva Turley, who has been
a regular guest on "Quirks and Quarks."

While I was visiting her office at the Hospital for Sick
Children in Toronto she asked, "Would you like to see my
new lab?"

She had just been given the facility to continue her work on
cancer genes. The new lab benches gleamed, fume hoods
shined brightly; there wasn't a single spot of spilled chemicals
anywhere. There was also no sign of equipment or people.

"It's nice, but it looks a little empty," I said, trying not to
stifle her enthusiasm.

"Oh they're still building it. Come back in a week and it will
look quite different."

Dr. Turley is known for her fundamental work at the Mani-
toba Institute of Cell Biology in Winnipeg, where she discovered the importance of a cancer-causing gene called RHAMM,
which controls a common cancer gene called RAS. Her efforts
had paid off because she was recruited to the Hospital for Sick

Children in Toronto and given the freedom to chose a top-notch team.

RAS genes are believed to be master switches that trigger the sequence of events leading to colon, pancreatic, breast and other forms of cancer. When RAS becomes mutated it instructs the cell to divide aggressively and spread, which is the first step on the road to cancer. Dr. Turley and her team hope to block the action of the RAS genes using RHAMM and prevent the growth of tumours. Early work shows that the tumours can be stopped from multiplying and from spreading although they can't be destroyed.

Another huge breakthrough came when one of the genes involved in the growth of cancer was identified. It's called P53 and its job is to put the brakes on runaway reproduction. Some cancer cells are missing this gene so they just keep on growing and growing. It's fine for cells to do that when we are young, but it's supposed to stop at a certain point. At the moment of conception the two cells that join to start our life, the sperm and egg, must multiply at a phenomenal rate to grow an entire body out of something that starts out too small to be seen with the naked eye. After we are born, the body has all the parts but they need to grow bigger, so cells keep dividing and reproducing, growing longer limbs, larger organs until the body reaches full size at maturity. Around that time, the P53 gene sends its message to cells to slow down their frantic pace and spend the rest of life maintaining the same number. Reproducing only happens when cells need to be repaired or replaced. P53 acts both as a brake to slow down cell division and as damage control to repair wounds. If this emergency brake was not in place, our bodies would continue growing past maturity until we became giants and collapsed under our own weight.

Tumour cells don't have this emergency brake; they are lacking P53 so they continue growing out of control. Geneticists would like to insert new genes into cancer cells so they will either stop growing or commit suicide. An overactive P53 gene can cause cells to self-destruct. The challenge is getting the gene into the nucleus of every cancer cell in a tumour, which is like trying to give a million microscopic injections. There is no way to do that with needles but it turns out that nature has provided an injection system for us . . . the virus.

Viruses are alien invaders. They are so primitive some people argue that they are not even alive. Unable to reproduce on their own, they survive by taking over the genetic machinery of a cell and reprogramming it so the cell produces more viruses. These microscopic hijackers are very effective at entering the body and injecting their own DNA into cells, like a vandal who records over your favourite video. Already a link has been established between viruses and cancer. The sexually transmitted papaloma virus has been found to be responsible for cervical cancer and a herpes virus has been linked to multiple myeloma, cancer of the bone marrow. The viruses don't actually cause the cancer, they somehow trigger the mechanisms that make ordinary cells become cancerous. But while viruses can be enemies they can also be allies. In a novel experiment in California, a virus is being used to stop cancer.

Dr. Frank McCormick at the University of California in San Francisco has pioneered a clever technique where viruses are hijacked to work for us by carrying new DNA to cancer cells. Viruses behave like microscopic needles, injecting beneficial DNA into individual cells. That means geneticists can use the viruses as couriers to deliver specific DNA to cancer cells and change their behaviour.

Dr. McCormick begins with a normal cold virus which is

very good at spreading rapidly throughout the body. To make sure the patients don't get a cold from the virus, it is stripped of its harmful characteristics. The modified form, now called an adenovirus, is given the P53 gene we want it to deliver to the cancer cells. The viruses are injected into the body and do what they normally do, infect the body's cells, but this time the infection is very specific—the virus goes only after cancer cells. Normal healthy cells already have P53 so they are not bothered.

The idea is that the new P53 from the adenovirus will enter the cancer cells and put the brakes on their runaway repro- duction. At the same time, the virus commands the cell to make more virus so the infection spreads. Finally, the end result of a viral infection is that the cell dies, so this weak cold virus ends up killing cancer cells.

So far, this techniques seems to work . . . in mice. Very little work has been done on humans. Actually it works better than expected because this gene can do more than stop cells from reproducing, it can kill them as well. As part of its role in damage control, if P53 finds damage in the DNA, it switches on a program that tells the cell to commit suicide. Experi- ments have shown that tumours shrink considerably after the viral infection.

The final benefit of using a virus is that the body's immune system sees it as an invader and goes after it. If the virus is attached to a cancer cell, that cell is attacked as well. So it looks as though a simple injection with a virus attacks cancer cells on three fronts, and they are killed by the virus, the P53 gene and the body's immune system. Sounds pretty effective.

But before we get too excited about this idea, Dr. McCormick cautions that there are drawbacks. First, the tech- nique only works on solid tumours, the lumps, and the injec- tion has to go directly into them. The technique does not work on cancer cells that spread throughout the body. Second, experiments in mice can only be taken so far because P53 is a human gene, so it may behave differently in people. Finally, since the virus is an invader, the body's immune system may attack it before it gets to the cancer cells. Still, it's a strange irony that while we haven't found a cure for the common cold, the common cold may help us cure cancer.

The link between viruses and cancer is an opportunity to develop the holy grail of cancer research, a vaccine. When a virus is involved in cancer, the vaccine can be aimed against the virus itself. But that's an indirect approach. A vaccine aimed directly at the cancer is preferable, but more difficult. Vaccines work by alerting the body's immune system that there is an invader. Our natural defence system is a remarkably efficient army of white blood cells that seek out and destroy anything that doesn't belong. The trick is letting the immune system know what the enemy looks like. A vaccine is a small sample of a disease-causing virus that has been neutralized so it does no harm, but when it is injected into the blood, the immune system sees it as an invader. Once educated, the white blood cells will attack anything that looks similar. It's a great system, but it doesn't work with cancer because cancer cells are not invaders from the outside; they come from the body itself so they are not recognized by the immune system. So the trick to developing a cancer vaccine is to make cancer cells look foreign, or put a flag on them so the immune system can be alerted. It's like a parking lot full of cars where one of them has a dead battery. They all look alike until the lights are turned on—then the faulty car shows up immediately.

There are a number of approaches to tagging cancer cells.

Our immune system identifies cells by their outer skin. Along the outer surface of a cell are molecules that the immune system uses like fingerprints to identify those that belong to the body and those that are alien. Since cancer cells came from the body, they wear the same skin, have the same fingerprints as normal cells so they remain invisible. But the immune system is also wary of slight changes in the normal pattern. Too much of one thing can be a sign that the cell is unhealthy so the immune system will get rid of it. Researchers are trying to find specific molecules on cancer cells, clone them into large numbers in the laboratory and make them into a vaccine. When these overloaded vaccines are put back into the body, the immune system is alerted to that molecule and begins to destroy everything that carries it. The hope is that the immune system will at the same time also destroy cancer cells carrying that molecule.

Dr. Stephen Rosenberg at the National Cancer Institute in Bethesda, Maryland, has had very promising results with a vaccine against melanoma, or skin cancer. Almost half of his patients given the vaccine had their immune-system response and their cancer reduced. However these people were in the final stages of the disease with only seven or eight months to live. Dr. Rosenberg says at this point the vaccine should be used along with chemotherapy and radiation as a cleanup for those cells that escaped treatment.

While the results are encouraging, the vaccine only works with one type of cancer. Developing a different vaccine for every cancer is a monumental job. The other difficulty goes back to this annoying ability of cancer to change. That's the problem when dealing with mutants—they are very adaptable to new situations. Cancer cells have found clever ways to avoid the immune system. If there is a telltale molecule on the surface of a cancer cell that is acting as a flag for the immune system, the cell stops making it, essentially cloaking itself in a disguise. Mutant cells grow so quickly they can outrun the immune system. They can change so quickly that by the time a vaccine is developed, the cells could have mutated into another form making the vaccine useless.

The biggest fear in developing a cancer vaccine is triggering the immune system to attack the body's own cells. If it can't tell the difference between cancer cells and healthy ones, when we train it to go after the bad guys it could go after the good guys as well and you end up with an autoimmune disease like arthritis or lupus. The last thing scientists want is to make the body attack itself. Fortunately this problem hasn't shown up in vaccine trials so far.

It would be nice to have a vaccine that could be given to children along with their other vaccination shots and which would protect them against cancer for the rest of their lives, but a magic bullet is not likely to happen. Cancer is too complicated a disease to be beaten by one solution.

For every medical breakthrough I saw, one question always remained: "When will this be available?" The answers ranged from "We're just beginning clinical trials" to "Five to ten years from now." I hear these qualifications all the time: it's standard practice in medical science to be cautious. Usually those responses are a sign of encouragement, but now they took on a different meaning. I was about to experience what it's like to know that there are breakthroughs on the horizon, but they are not arriving fast enough to help someone who needs them now.

Each time I returned to the hospital, Gerry looked thinner, even if I was only away for a couple of days. But his spirits were still high and he had many questions about what I was finding out in cancer research. It gave him hope that even if the laser treatment didn't work, there would be some other miracle of modern science that would stop the cancerous cells from destroying his brain.

I continued to hear about the other miracle approaches, such as "anti-angiogenesis." At the Sunnybrook Medical Centre in Toronto, Dr. Bob Kerbel described an approach to fighting cancer that was discovered by Judah Folkman in Boston and does not involve attacking genes. It's an attempt to starve cancer tumours by cutting off their blood supply. Since tumours are growing rapidly, they need a lot of extra food. Angiogenesis is a process where the tumours sprout extra blood vessels that extend out like tentacles to ensure a steady supply of nutrients for the tumour. These extra blood vessels also provide extra escape routes for the renegade cells that in the later stage separate from the tumour and wander throughout the body.

The keys to turning on the production of these new blood lines are growth factors, hormones that stimulate rapid growth. Dr. Kerbel and his team are hoping to interfere with the production of the growth factors so the new blood vessels will not form, starving the tumour, like cutting off the supply lines to an army. Experiments in mice have shown that tumours actually become addicted to the growth factor so that when it is cut off, the tumour cells die as though going through withdrawal.

A number of drugs are being developed to interfere with the growth factor, including shark cartilage. A big advantage to this approach is that the blood vessels are not actually cancerous, so targeting them means there is less chance they will mutate and become resistant to the drugs. Results look promising, but again, these are only laboratory experiments and treatment for cancer patients is still many years off. There is also the usual list of hazards for this approach. The ability to grow extra blood vessels is not something we want to eliminate completely. It's a vital part of tissue repair when we cut or injure ourselves. If we couldn't grow new blood vessels, wounds would never heal. That means the drugs that stop this process must be delivered to the cancer cells only. Perhaps viruses can act as couriers here as well.

At the end of my interviews with cancer researchers, I usually mentioned my friend's situation and asked what they thought. At the mention of a brain tumour the response was almost always the same . . . brain cancer is extremely serious and there is not much that can be done about it beyond a certain point.

That turning point happened on the eve of Gerry's surgery. When I arrived to see him that day, several other visitors were in the room. I immediately sensed an uneasy feeling among the group. Gerry's wife, Carol, was misty-eyed. The doctors had performed a scan of his brain that morning to check on the condition of his tumour. They found that the cancer was spreading faster than they expected. Like tentacles from a jellyfish, the tumour was penetrating deeper into the recesses of his brain and out of reach of the laser beam. The operation was cancelled. There was nothing more that could be done. It seemed as though science had given up and signed off on his life.

We all know we're going to die and even accept the fact that it could happen tomorrow through some twist of fate. But knowing that there is a good chance, if we take care of ourselves, that we will see old age, we put aside those short-term possibilities and live with the sincere hope that our lives will be long and healthy. To be told that your life will end within weeks when you are still in your forties just doesn't fit with what we accept as our mortality. There must be a mistake, another opinion, another option that will reverse that unacceptable fact. We live in a world where anything is possible for a price. Mistakes are fixed, broken things are repaired, it's just a matter of finding the right person with the solution. There are specialists we can call on, people with alternatives: there is always a way out.

I could see all these thoughts flashing across my best friend's face and stood frustrated that all the scientific knowledge in the world could not stop these cancerous cells from taking over his brain. Everyone else in the room felt a similar helplessness and all of us struggled to accept the undeniable truth that our dear friend would be taken away by an insidious process. But our disbelief was nothing compared to that which showed on the face of the man who carried the cancer in his head. He turned to each of us with a desperately pleading look. "What's going on here? Am I dying? Can't we get a second opinion? Bob, isn't there some other kind of treatment available?"

None of us could answer. I will never forget the look of profound sadness and fear that washed over Gerry's face. It was the last time I ever saw him reaching out to anyone. Nature has such simple ways of humbling humanity. Tiny cells, barely visible to the eye, were growing and multiplying where they didn't belong and there was nothing anyone on the planet could do to stop them. I've never felt so helpless.

I was angry that science had led me to believe in false hopes. The view down a microscope or the shrinking of tumours in mice is a long way from the hospital bed. People like me who work in the media are constantly speaking with great optimism about new breakthroughs and exciting new discoveries in cancer research. We make it sound like tremendous strides are being made on the road to a cure, when in fact it's only the scientists who are excited. And they have a right to be. Scientific research is slow and tedious. Years of work bring only tiny steps forward. So many apparent breakthroughs turn out to be blind alleys. Science is based more on failures than successes, so any good result is worth celebrating. The people lying in bed read every new announcement with great anticipation, only to be disillusioned by the hard reality that breakthroughs will not be available until long after the disease has consumed them.

In the 1960s there was a television series called *Run For Your Life*. It was about a man who was told that he only had a year to live, maybe two. A very healthy Ben Gazzara bade farewell to his friends and family then headed off on exciting adventures where risk was not an issue. We all have that fantasy that we will somehow know the date of our death far enough in advance to pursue all those unfulfilled fantasies. The reality is that by the time people are told their life will end in the near future, they are already very sick.

Gerry asked if he could simply go home and be with his wife, but even that request was denied. The tumour was increasing the pressure on his brain and the doctors were concerned that it could cause a hemorrhage at any time. Even his simple choices had run out.

As I continued to conduct interviews with cancer specialists, it became more and more difficult to generate enthusiasm for a science that I knew could not help a friend. At one point I broke professional courtesy with Dr. Alistair Cunningham, a clinical psychologist at Princess Margaret Hospital who uses relaxation, self-awareness and visualization to help people diagnosed with serious cancer to cope with the reality of their disease. He was describing how a positive attitude helps people come to grips with the fact that they may not live to their next birthday when I blurted out, "What do you say to people who have been abandoned by the system, who are suddenly told that there is no hope and are left to die?"

I almost spat the question at him and immediately felt badly that I was taking my anger out on an innocent by-stander. As a psychiatrist he's surely seen a lot of anger. Leaning back slightly as though avoiding a punch, he astutely replied, "Obviously someone close to you has recently been diagnosed with terminal cancer."

"Yes," I replied, "someone very close."

As I attempted to regain my composure, the soft-spoken doctor explained the problem that often befalls families faced with terminal illness. Denial forces loved ones to say, "Everything's going to be all right, don't worry." It's natural to do that because we really do want everything to be fine. But avoiding the truth sets everyone, including the cancer patient, up for disappointment. When the reality of death finally sinks in, no one is prepared for it. Physicians sometimes fall into the same trap when dealing with patients. A healthier approach is to deal with the possibility of death early on and try to come to peace with it. There comes a point when everyone should think about the health of the patient rather than killing cancer cells. Making the most of the time remaining is a better service to the patient than living with false hope.

He was right, we do spend a lot of time pretending everything will return to normal when in fact cancer changes everything for everybody. But there was more to Dr. Cunningham's approach than just mind over matter. He seriously believes that the brain does have an effect on the body's ability to cope with disease and he changed his career to pursue it. Up until the early eighties Dr. Cunningham was one of the top immunologists in the country. He decided to change his career towards psychology because he believed there was a gap in the understanding of how the body deals with disease. He is also a cancer survivor.

It is now well accepted that the immune system, the nervous system and endocrine or hormone system are all connected. People under stress often get colds because the tension has lowered their immunity. People who are given dummy pills but still fell better, the so-called placebo effect, could be using their body's own resources to fight illness. In other words, a positive attitude makes a huge difference. One retired doctor I know who takes a somewhat grandmotherly approach to medicine told me, "Hugs and kisses are just as important as pills." We've all known since childhood the therapeutic benefits of a gentle, reassuring hug. Now science is finally accepting that there may be something to feeling good that goes beyond chemistry and molecular genetics.

Later I sat in on one of Dr. Cunningham's sessions along with about fifty cancer patients in a lecture theatre at the hospital. Some wore headbands or caps to cover their bald heads, a side effect of chemotherapy; some were a little pale; and all were just regular folk from a wide range of backgrounds who happened to have come down with a serious disease, in some cases terminal. I was surprised how many were my age and younger. While music played quietly in the background, everyone sat with eyes closed listening to the soft voice of Dr. Cunningham taking them through a relaxation exercise where they imagined themselves lying on a beach soaking in the warm rays of the Sun. He then worked a slow sequence down the body, relieving tension by isolating and relaxing one part at a time, starting at the top of the head and progressing down to the feet. The simple act of sitting still long enough to go through the sequence is relaxing in itself.

By the time he had the members of his audience slightly slumped in their seats looking half asleep, Dr. Cunningham did something I found uncommon. He asked everyone to visualize their cancer, to locate it in their body and feel its presence. He asked them to imagine it getting smaller, receding until it disappeared. He spoke of filling the space where the cancer was with energy, strength and positive feelings.

Visualizing the disease is accepting it, and imagining it shrinking away helps build strength to fight it. The will of the patient is a potent force against the ravages of disease and it makes a tremendous difference in maintaining quality of life during the illness. Too many people fall into black depression, spending their last days in misery.

A small study involving women with breast cancer showed how those who underwent psychotherapy lived twice as long as those who didn't.

After the session everyone was very calm and the people I spoke to unanimously agreed that they would rather know the truth about their condition than be told they would be cured. They also spoke of the value of group support from the other cancer patients. Not one of them seemed morbid about their future.

During my next visit with Gerry I tried to tell him about the effect of a positive attitude as well as other research about how the brain can make new connections and restore its mental capability when it is challenged. People who learn a new language or take up a musical instrument late in life are better able to fight off Alzheimer's disease. Autopsies on active people show their brains actually have more connections than those who plateau early and coast intellectually for the rest of their lives.

But Gerry would have none of it. He was angry that there wasn't a quicker solution, something that could get rid of the cancer for good. Telling him to have a positive attitude was placing everything on his shoulders when in fact he had done nothing wrong. Not being a psychotherapist, I didn't know how to respond, other than to feel even more helpless.

Meanwhile the war on cancer continues on many different fronts with new molecular weapons. While the surgical knives and radiation machines will still continue to play a role, more weapons will come in a needle. Vaccines, tumour suppressors, viruses will attack the cancer from its very core. Along with the new weapons there is a new attitude towards the disease, an attitude of co-existence rather than conflict. As with diabetes, and perhaps one day AIDS, it may be possible to control the disease rather than try to destroy it. Our brute-force, kill-the-enemy approach often results in killing the patient as well. When the disease stays at low levels in the body it appears to do no harm, so why try to get rid of it completely?

It was encouraging to hear the excitement among researchers who described how it may one day be possible to actually live with the disease but not suffer the harmful effects. But while we look to the scientists for solutions, there is still one major factor that contributes to the spread of cancer and that is the way we live. During one interview with a scientist studying lung cancer, he said, "You know, we've been working for years trying to beat this cancer, but none of this work would be necessary if people just stopped smoking." Ninety-five percent of lung cancer is triggered by tobacco.

Toronto has been trying to enforce no-smoking bylaws for years amid loud opposition. For a few weeks one summer a law was introduced banning smoking in all bars and restaurants. For a week it was actually possible to eat food that didn't taste like smoke. But the outcry from smokers and bar owners was so loud that the law was repealed. I will refrain from launching into my anti-smoking rant because I was once a culprit. I quit because I got scared when I ran out of breath running. I don't know what it will take to scare everyone into thinking about cancer. Perhaps it's because sick people always seem to be someone else, someone distant. When it hits close to home you think a little differently about how easy it is to be selected as the next one to go, the trauma to friends and family and the very real possibility that you could be next.

During my regular visits to see Gerry in the following weeks, I wondered about the great roulette wheel somewhere that decides who lives and who dies. I couldn't help asking myself, "Why him and not me?" He didn't do anything wrong, cancer just ate his brain.

From that point on Gerry began to shut down communication. Somehow, through whatever process only the dying know, he had reconciled within himself the fact that he was leaving for good. They say that when tumours grow in the brain, mental facilities remain largely intact. I kept that in mind as his responses became nothing more than slight nods while he never made eye contact. Soon his eyes were almost always closed as he drifted in and out of sleep. But I believed he was still present in mind and he did continue to acknowledge my presence whenever I dropped in. Eventually that acknowledgment was nothing more than a change in breathing when I told him stories from the good old days.

I've dealt with death many times—my father died when I was sixteen, I lost three classmates around the same time, I've carried the coffins of aunts and uncles. But this was the first time I was actually seeing the process of dying happen before my eyes. An unseen force slowly drains the vitality out of a once-animated body. Skin settles onto bones, movement diminishes, breathing becomes a shallow reflex.

Around 9:30 on the morning of the final day I received a phone call from Gerry's brother Bill who informed me that they were not expecting him to make it past noon that day. I was booked solid with interviews until 3:00 in the afternoon. I said I would get there as soon as possible. Throughout the day I was saying in the back of my mind, "Hang on, pal, I'm on my way."

By 3:15, I was running down the hospital corridor. A few family members were standing outside the room. Bill said, "He doesn't look very good, but he's still alive." It's difficult to describe a barely breathing corpse. It certainly didn't bear any resemblance to the person I knew, just an assembly of bones covered with loose grey flesh, eyes half-open and unfocused, sunk deeply into the sockets of the skull, a shallow pant coming from the partly open gap that used to be a mouth. Sitting beside the bed I took the skeletal hand in mine and said, "You're already cold. Thanks for waiting." I don't completely recall what else I talked about during those last moments, except before leaving I found myself saying, "See you on the other side." It sounded strange coming from my own mouth since I'm not particularly religious, but it felt better than saying goodbye.

As I stepped into the elevator on the way out, an alarm sounded in the nursing station. I didn't look back.

CODA: NORTHERN LIGHTS, SOUTHERN SKIES

The view from down here

STARS SPREAD ACROSS THE moonless sky like diamonds tossed over black velvet. The brilliant points of light barely twinkle through the –40-degree air. Wrapped in a parka, snow pants, mitts and mukluks, I stand waist-deep in powder snow under a sky so deep and air so silent that I could be an astronaut in space. It's my last night in Yellowknife, the Northern Lights Capital of the World, and I'm ready for a cosmic light show.

Northern lights are an opportunity to see the invisible, the unseen part of our atmosphere and its wild interaction with the atmosphere of the Sun. Space was once thought to be truly empty, a perfect vacuum. We now know that what appears to be the black void of space is filled with exotic particles whizzing about at unbelievable speeds, twisted magnetic fields, all wrapping around each other, exchanging energy and producing, among many other things, the eerie glow of the northern lights.

Aurora borealis, or aurora australis if you live in the Southern Hemisphere, is a symphony of light conducted by the Sun and played out in the thin upper atmosphere of the Earth. A swift wind of electrically charged particles blows outward from the Sun then, guided by the magnetic field of the Earth, heads towards the North and South Poles where it slams into our air and releases its energy as an eerie glow.

Astronauts who have flown on the space shuttle often comment on how thin the Earth's atmosphere is compared to the size of the planet—about the thickness of fuzz on a peach. When you look out the window of a speeding space shuttle orbiting three hundred kilometres above the Earth, sunsets only last a few seconds, when the atmosphere becomes a thin haze clinging to the curve of the horizon, a multicoloured band less than half the width of a little finger. Above this gassy film is nothing but the cold blackness of space. But there is more to the Earth's atmosphere than meets the astronaut's eye.

More than 90 percent of the air, the part we breathe, the part that contains clouds and weather, is within twenty kilometres of the surface. However, it doesn't just end abruptly the way it appears to from space. In fact there is no clearly defined upper edge to our atmosphere, it just sort of gradually fades out at extreme altitude. Traces of the atmosphere can still be found as high as 1,500 kilometres, more than three times the height of a space shuttle orbit. That means technically the shuttle does not actually fly in space—it's still within the atmosphere of the Earth.

During early flights of the space shuttle, scientists noticed that there was a glow coming from the tail section that was especially visible at night. It turned out to be an air glow caused by the shuttle's speed as it ran into traces of air. Travelling at 29,000 km/h the body of the shuttle rips the air apart creating a greenish glow in the process. In effect, the shuttle produces its own miniature version of northern lights by virtue of its speed through the same part of the upper atmosphere where the real northern lights appear.

There isn't a lot of air at those altitudes; it's more than 100,000 times thinner than the stuff that fills our lungs. Up there molecules are so far apart they take several seconds to run into each other, whereas those near the ground are in almost constant contact. But even though the air in the upper reaches of our atmosphere is almost too thin to even be called air, there is still enough of it to drag satellites and space stations out of orbit. It is within this tenuous region, above one hundred kilometres, that the northern lights find their home.

The curtains of light flickering across the sky are an awesome sight, witnessed by humans for tens of thousands of years. They are mentioned in Chinese records from 2600 BC; Inuit legends from the north tell of sky dwellers; and Maori legends from New Zealand describe the light as the glow from a great fire lit by ancestors floating in distant canoes. Today eco-tours carry enthralled tourists to the Arctic to marvel at the subtle beauty of the ghostly light that often blankets the sky from horizon to horizon.

Out alone on the frozen lake north of Yellowknife I was fortunate to have the clear skies all to myself. It was also the only clear night of my trip. The Arctic sky provided a transparent window to the universe. But that transparency is deceiving, for unseen to my eyes were the long tentacles of the Sun's atmosphere that reach across vast distances completely engulfing the Earth in a cosmic storm of invisible particles.

The idea that something pervades the blackness of space has been around since ancient times. Aristotle spoke about the ether, a transparent medium through which all the planets and stars travelled. Ancient astronomers puzzled over the strange behaviour of comets, which always keep their tails pointed away from the Sun regardless of which way they are travelling. Once a comet swings around the Sun and begins its journey back out to deep space, it travels tail first, as though there is some kind of wind that keeps the tail pointed in one direction like a flag in a stiff breeze. We had to send spacecraft well beyond Earth to prove that such a wind does exist. The source of the wind is the Sun.

One of the experiments carried to the Moon by the first astronauts on *Apollo 11* was a plain sheet of aluminum foil that was simply hung out like a piece of laundry during the seven hours the astronauts were hopping around making those famous giant leaps. The foil was then folded up and brought back to Earth where scientists shone a powerful light through it, exposing thousands of microscopic holes that had been punched through them by the speeding particles. Since then, probes to Venus, Mars and the other planets have found the wind blowing out from the Sun in all directions with a force that sends it well beyond Pluto; in fact no one knows exactly where it stops.

It's hard to fathom the energy that could produce such a wind. Then again, it's hard to fathom just about anything about our Sun, it's so much grander in scale than anything human. If the Sun was half the size of this page, the entire Earth would be smaller than the period at the end of this sentence. Every second a million tons of material is blown off the surface of the Sun, an amount as insignificant to the Sun as the loss of thousands of skin cells shed by your body every day. From the unimaginably violent surface of our Sun, atoms are torn to pieces and blown into space at 400 kilometres a second, 1.5 million km/h per hour. The stream of electrically charged protons and electrons race across interplanetary space covering the 150 million kilometres between the Sun and Earth in only two days. Their arrival is announced by our upper atmosphere, which glows green and red when the wind from space blows down from above.

In the same way that a space shuttle orbiting the Earth flies through the tenuous upper layers of the atmosphere, the Earth orbiting the Sun ploughs through the solar wind, an extension of the outer atmosphere of the Sun. Occasionally, unbelievable flares erupt off the surface of the Sun, sending more material towards the Earth, including x-ray radiation thousands of times more powerful that any exposure you get from dental or chest x-rays. These somewhat unpredictable flares were a concern during the Apollo missions to the Moon. If a flare erupted while they were outside on the lunar surface the astronauts, exposed to the full force of the Sun's fury, would have little chance of survival. Fortunately for us on Earth our magnetic bubble protects us from flares, although not completely. Flares can shake the Earth's magnetic field like a bubble in a breeze. The up-and-down motion of such a large magnetic field acts like a huge generator producing electric currents in the ground or in long power lines. Hydro-Québec was nearly knocked out in the late eighties by a solar flare that tripped circuit breakers in the lines running south from the newly completed James Bay Project. Flares have also knocked out communication satellites including Canada's *Anik 1*.

Still, this blasting breeze is totally invisible to our eyes . . . except when it fuels the fires of the northern lights.

Trudging through the deep snow, I try to get away from the artificial glow coming from the city of Yellowknife. I've seen northern lights before—but never under the clear Arctic skies. I hope to see the rich colours in the sky this region is famous for. Yellowknife calls itself the Northern Lights Capital of the World and I want to find out why.

Aurorae usually come in three colours—green, red and

blue, depending on the gas in the atmosphere giving off the light. When a charged particle from the Sun runs into an atom of oxygen in our air, the atom absorbs the energy for a short time, which puts the atom into an excited state. It's like putting food that's too hot in your mouth: you can hold onto it for a short time, but then you want to spit it out. And that's essentially what the atom does. It spits out the energy it absorbed and in the same way food coming out of your mouth looks different than when it went in, the energy that comes out of the atom is a different form of energy, a photon of light. That's what we see from the ground. The glow of the northern lights is countless billions of atoms and molecules high in the atmosphere spitting light. The colour of the light depends on the type of atom that spits it out. Oxygen gives off green light; it can also give off red depending on the amount of energy it has absorbed. Nitrogen releases blue light. Some gases are better at this than others which is why you don't usually see all the colours of the rainbow in an aurora display. The gases used in neon signs are of course neon for red light and argon for green and blue.

At least that's the theory on what it takes to see the northern lights. The other criterion that needs to be satisfied is that you need to go north to see them, and I thought I had taken care of that by travelling to the Northwest Territories. An invitation to visit communities across this country, especially in the north, is something I never refuse and always enjoy. In Yellowknife, scientists at the Prince of Wales Northern Heritage Centre showed me thousand-year-old hand tools made by the ancient Thule people who populated the North for thousands of years. I was fed caribou and bear meat at a Dene camp in the bush then taken deep underground where miners showed me how they coaxed gold out of the rock. The northern lights were a bonus and I didn't need a guide.

The northern and southern lights look like curtains across the sky but they are actually complete rings thousands of kilometres wide that form a glowing headband and ankle bracelet for the Earth. They are held in position at the top and bottom of the globe by the planet's magnetic field.

You were probably forced as a kid in grade-school science class to sprinkle iron filings over a bar magnet. The little pieces of iron lined up forming a looping pattern that looks like an apple cut in half. The lines run down both sides of the magnet then curl in at either end until they touch the north and south poles. Most kids find the effect interesting at first then just want to throw the iron shavings at each other. But that apple shape formed by the magnet is the reason northern lights happen where they do. The lines are really like fences that mark off fields where the magnetic effect is felt. When you are in a magnetic field, you are on the property of the magnet and it will affect you.

The same shape that you made with iron shavings in your childhood science class surrounds the entire Earth. It's what steers compass needles everywhere. Rising straight up from the north and south magnetic poles, the Earth's magnetic field lines arch high above the top and bottom of the planet looping down the sides as though there is a huge bar magnet buried in the centre of the Earth. In fact, the liquid iron core of our planet generates powerful electric currents that produce the field we experience on the surface. The field lines extend 65,000 kilometres in space, forming a huge magnetic bubble, a bubble that is our first line of defence against the blast of the solar wind.

If you could see the magnetic bubble around the Earth, the magnetosphere, it would look like a huge teardrop. The side facing the Sun is rounded and a long tail extends beyond the orbit of the Moon on the night side.

There is a rule in physics that all sub-atomic particles carrying an electric charge cannot cross lines of magnetic force, but can only flow along them. They can't cross a fence but they can run alongside one. When the charged electrons and protons from the Sun run into the side of the Earth's magnetic field anywhere near the equator, they run north and south parallel to the surface following the field lines. They spiral as they go as though they are trying to jump over the fence.

Most of the particles in the solar wind flow around our magnetic bubble and continue on past the Earth like water flowing around a boulder in a stream. If we didn't have this magnetic protection, the solar wind would smash into the upper atmosphere, blasting atoms and molecules of our air into space. In no time at all our atmosphere would be stripped right off the planet. This is one theory of what happened to Mars, where there is almost no magnetic field and almost no atmosphere left. Only heavy carbon dioxide remains on Mars today, possibly because all the lighter gases were literally blown away by the solar wind. A similar phenomenon may explain the mainly carbon-dioxide atmosphere on Venus, a planet also lacking a magnetic field.

On their way around our planet, some of the solar wind particles become trapped in our magnetic field, following the magnetic field lines towards the North and South Poles. In the same way the iron shavings arched around the ends of the bar magnet until they stood straight up at the north and south poles, the magnetic field lines of the Earth guide the solar wind particles in a curve downwards towards the poles, down to where it meets the excitable atmosphere. That's why you only see aurorae at high latitudes and not at the equator.

This then is the aurora, particles born on the Sun crashing into atoms of air on the edge of space, giving the northern lights their ghostly hue. It's hard to believe that the glow in the sky on Earth is from activity on the Sun. It's something like the soft glow on a wall when logs burn in a fireplace except this fire is on a star 150 million kilometres away.

I stomp through deep snow for twenty minutes trying to reach a spot where the city lights are blocked by hills and trees. With no moon to cover their brightness, the stars reach all the way down to the horizon. If I was going to see northern lights, this was the place to be. Drawing on my scientific (ahem) knowledge of the night sky, I locate the constellations that point the way to the North Star and face that direction, hoping to see the beautiful curtains of light this city is famous for.

The aurora borealis is one of the most breathtaking sights in nature. Like a veil hung from heaven, the ghostly hues form a drape complete with bright trim along the bottom hemline.

From cities at high latitudes such as Yellowknife, aurorae are almost a nightly event. Although they sometimes appear to reach right down to the ground, all the activity creating the glow begins about a hundred kilometres up and extends all the way into the fringes of space which probably makes them the largest single structure you can see on the Earth. I am hoping to see drapery formations, or rays extending up from the horizon which gather overhead around what appears to be a dark hole in the sky. Perhaps I will catch them flickering like firelight, or even hear the crackling sounds, which according to legend can only be heard by the most sensitive ears.

But alas, the sky, as beautiful as it is, remains jet black. Walking through the deep powder snow dressed like a little kid in a snowsuit has been quite an effort for a city boy. Before heading back I decide to rest and do a little star gazing. The snow is so deep and soft I just fall backwards with a whump and lie still, my own breathing the only sound breaking the total silence.

The opportunity to experience complete quiet is becoming quite rare. Humans have become so good at generating noise with our technology, music, the nattering of our own voices that it's hard to get away from it all. I lie there thinking about the snow-covered rocks and how much time they spend here in the north without sound. The stars overhead exist in a universe of silence since sound doesn't travel in space. Holding my breath I imagine myself on the frozen polar ice cap of Mars, or one of the ice-covered moons of Jupiter. The snowy landscape would look very similar and the same constellations would hang in the sky on those other worlds. For a few moments I'm an astronaut exploring the frozen moons and planets out there in the cold depths of the solar system. But out there I would not see any northern or southern lights draping the sky.

Earth is the only place where you can stand on the ground and look up at them. Some planets—Mercury, Venus and Mars—don't have aurorae at all. A planet needs that special combination of magnetic field and thick atmosphere to produce the glow in the sky. Mercury has a magnetic field but almost no air. Venus has incredibly dense air but almost no magnetic field, and even if aurorae did appear there they would be obscured by thick clouds that perpetually enshroud the entire planet. Mars has neither much air nor magnetic field. The big planets—Jupiter, Saturn, Uranus and Neptune—have aurorae but those planets are made of gas so there is no solid ground to stand on. I guess you could float in a balloon on those planets, but that's an awful lot of trouble to go through. Once again the Earth turns out to be a special place where humans get some of the best views.

But obviously not this night in Yellowknife.

Resigning myself to the fact that I'm not going to see the light show, I get up, turn around and stop dead in my tracks. There, spread across the entire southern sky, is the most beautiful aurora I've ever seen. What an idiot. Here I am, Mr. Science, on a personal mission to see the northern lights, not realizing that when you go north, the lights are south of you. The particles from the Sun don't actually reach the North Pole. The ring they form around the top of the world can extend more than thirty degrees south, especially when there is a lot of activity on the Sun.

The headband around the top of the Earth is oval-shaped and off-centre, like a tilted tiara. The force of the solar wind blows it off to one side towards the night side of the Earth. The amount of the offset depends on how active the Sun is. Every eleven years the Sun becomes covered in sunspots, areas of strong magnetic activity that increase the strength of the solar wind. During sunspot maximum the aurora ring is pushed much farther south. It turned out that the time I was in Yellowknife the Sun was in a period of sunspot maximum, so the aurora ring looped down south of the city.

At first sight, the aurora seems to be hanging motionless in the sky but if you stare for a few moments without blinking, you can catch the slow wave motion passing through its form, like a giant flag slowly flapping. Green, red and blue apparitions appear and disappear as though they are falling as liquid out of the blackness above, then evaporate into nothingness. You can see why the ancient Greeks called the aurora "Blood Rain."

Once your eyes become accustomed to the subtle glow, you catch rapid flickers shooting upwards like tongues of fire lapping against the side of a log. The flickers are so quick they almost elude the eye. In Scottish legends, the rhythmic motions of the night lights were merry dancers of the sky.

So I did see a beautiful display of northern lights that night. I'm sure glad no one saw me out there on the wrong side of town looking north.

READING LIST

Barrow, John D. *Between Inner Space and Outer Space.* New York: Oxford University Press, 1999.

Bright, Chris. *Life Out of Bounds: Bioinvasion in a Borderless World.* New York: W.W. Norton & Company, 1998.

Caidin, Martin, and Jay Barbree. *Destination Mars: In Art, Myth, and Science.* Toronto: Penguin Canada, 1997.

Dickenson, Terrence. *The Universe and Beyond.* Toronto: Firefly Books, 1999.

Ferris, Timothy. *The Whole Shebang.* New York: Simon & Schuster, 1997.

Hawking, Stephen, and Roger Penrose. *The Nature of Space and Time.* Princeton, NJ: Princeton University Press, 1996.

Krauss, Lawrence M. *Fear of Physics.* New York: Basic Books, 1993.

Maddox, John. *What Remains to be Discovered: Mapping the Secrets of the Universe, the Origins of Life, and the Future of the Human Race.* New York: The Free Press, Simon & Shuster Inc., 1998.

McWhirthers, Norris. *The Book of Millennium Records.* London: Virgin Publishing, 1999.

Newton, Roger G. *Thinking About Physics.* Princeton, NJ: Princeton University Press, 2000.

Ridley, Matt. *Genome: The Autobiography of a Species in 23 Chapters.* New York: HarperCollins Publishers, 1999.

Sagan, Carl. *Murmurs of Earth: The Voyager Interstellar Record.* New York: Random House, 1978.

———. *Pale Blue Dot: A Vision of the Human Future in Space.* New York: Random House, 1994.

Scarth, Alwyn. *Vulcan's Fury: Man Against the Volcano.* New Haven, CT: Yale University Press, 1999.

Shirley, Donna. *Managing Martians.* New York: Broadway Books, 1998.

Smoot, George, and Keay Davidson. *Wrinkles in Time.* New York: William and Morrow and Company, 1993.

Verkaik, Arjen, and Jerrine Verkaik. *Under the Whirlwind.* Elmwood, Ont.: Whirlwind Books, 1997.

Weinberg, Robert A. *One Renegade Cell: How Cancer Begins.* New York: Basic Books, 1998.

INDEX